ALCHEMY
of the
AFTERLIFE

A Memoir

LINDA KINNAMON, RN

Flatirons Press

ISBN-13: 978-0-9967329-0-1
ISBN-10: 09967329-0-X

Library of Congress Control Number:
2015914458

Book design by *Christopher Derrick, for Unauthorized Media*
Cover design by *Launie Perry, red letter creative*

Flatirons Press
Boulder

First Edition

Printed in the United States of America

For Mama

To Debbie~
Enjoy every
moment of life!
Linda
Kimicina

"Some words will never be spoken

Some stories will never be told.

This is the age you are broken

Or turned into gold."

— Antonia Michaelis

CHAPTER 1

One eye fluttered, opening only enough to allow a view of my own eyelashes. Slowly, like doors rusted on their hinges, I opened both eyes, ready to slam them shut if anything or anyone was looking back. This peekaboo technique has always served me well when watching horror movies. I've just never needed it first thing in the morning, in my own bedroom.

When the initial glance revealed no one except the snoring cat at the foot of the bed, I grew brave. As I rolled over to my back, Twister raised her head to indicate her disapproval at being disturbed, immediately settling back down to dreams of mice or birds or whatever it is cats dream about. Biscuit, the dog, remained asleep in her usual spot on the rug beside me.

Surely, if there were cause for alarm one of the animals would show concern, or at least wake up.

My hand slid across the bed, touching only cool sheets. Kevin was traveling again. I would feel safer if he were here. Would he be aware of it, too? While he never doubted my experiences, he usually didn't share them either.

Acknowledging the tightness in my chest, holding my breath forever was not going to be an option. I exhaled and breathed in hungrily, needing air, no matter what accompanied it.

Perfume. It was still there. It was not a scented candle or potpourri, which I don't have in the bedroom anyway. It was perfume. I could smell it just as clearly as if I were walking through the fragrance section of a department store. It was present and undeniable. How could that be, unless someone freshly misted with scent was walking past me or spritzing an atomizer into the air? Who or what had brought it into my bedroom? And why?

I had been awake, eyes still closed, reluctant to start another day when I first smelled it. I was listening to the traffic report on the radio at my bedside. I had also been attempting to pray for my patients, something I'm not good at, even when I'm not multi-tasking by listening to reports of fender benders and stalled cars. Slowly sitting up in bed, I could not be dreaming perfume. Besides, I wasn't sure I'd ever dreamed a scent.

I pulled the quilt up to my throat, aware that someone could be looking back at me. Again, I breathed deeply of the perfume filling the air. I couldn't identify the fragrance, but then the only bottle of perfume I have is at least five years old. More importantly, I couldn't think of anyone, living or dead, whoever smelled this heavenly.

It did smell heavenly, and peaceful, if peace could somehow become a scent. No matter how it came to be in my bedroom, I could no longer fear it. That would be like fearing happiness or sunshine.

With both eyes now open wide, I ventured a glance around the room. The windows were still dressed for night, the row of white shades pulled down tight to the sills. The pair of overstuffed rocking chairs sat undisturbed facing the windows, their blue and green flowered upholstery pattern becoming distinguishable in the brightening light. The oak wardrobe inherited from Kevin's grandmother sat facing the foot of the bed. On it was the mantel clock I had as a lone relic of my childhood and my family history. On both sides of the clock, brass-framed photos sat in orderly array. The walls evolved from gray to sage green, the color awakened by daybreak.

I didn't see or hear anything out of the ordinary. Growing braver or more curious or some combination of the two, I pulled the covers off and slid my bare feet to the cold floorboards. The bedside rug was still occupied by my lightly snoring guard dog. As I padded across the floor, the scent wafted away. In the past couple of minutes, I had journeyed from uncertainty and near fear to delight at the fragrance's beauty and accompanying sensation of peace.

My chest rose again as I sucked in as much air as my lungs could hold. I held it for a moment, then exhaled my disappointment. Closing my eyes, I willed the perfume to come back. Of course, I couldn't conjure perfume. Conjuring is part of a skill set better suited to movies and books than real life. Receiving encoded messages, however, has worked its way into my job description over time.

As the white shades continued to brighten in the growing morning light, my mind searched for explanations that could not be found. Where the fragrance went, I did not know, any more than I knew where it came from or how it came to be. Understanding was as elusive as the smell of perfume itself. It was just there, and then gone. Despite my lack of understanding, I felt calm. Peace was all that lingered.

CHAPTER 2

Having been awakened by the scent of perfume rather than coffee, I headed to the kitchen. I picked up the phone and punched in my office voice mail number before even turning on the light. Coffee. Must have coffee. As I began scooping the granules into the filter, counting the spoonfuls to myself, "One, two, three..." I was also hearing, "You have twelve new messages. Message received at five p.m. yesterday..."

Six spoons, no, it's four spoons and five o'clock.

"Hi, Team Four, you have a new admission..."

Was that four spoons or Team Four? No, wait. It's both.

Eventually, I eyeballed the amount of coffee and water, pressed brew, and turned my attention back to the other eleven messages. The warm smell of brewing coffee began to fill the air as I listened to bits and pieces of my voice mail messages. As I inhaled the faintly hazelnut scent, anticipating the warmth it would bring on a cold morning, I saw the coffee dripping and heard the gurgle of the pot brewing and the splash as the dark liquid landed in the waiting carafe. The smell was predictable, just as predictable as the heat and taste of the beverage. My mind kept wandering away from the messages and coffee, back to the fragrance in my bedroom. How could I smell perfume when there was none? It wasn't merely a trace or a fleeting whiff. It had been as real and recognizable as the coffee was at this moment.

Fortunately, none of my voice mail messages seemed to be pertinent. Most were admissions for other teams in other parts of Dallas, or reports on hospital patients I would never meet. There was only one admission for the north team today, and it couldn't be mine. We received our assignments primarily based on geography. The new patient lived in the Dallas suburb of Sachse. Marilyn, one of my teammates, lived in Sachse, so there could be no question of the assignment. This would be Marilyn's admission, not mine. I felt a bit relieved because I already had sixteen patients. Still watching the coffee drip, I listened to the admission report anyway. With Marilyn's propensity for calling in sick with a hangnail, I would probably visit this patient sooner or later.

"Bonnie H. lives in Sachse with her husband, Jim. She has

been undergoing treatment for cancer, but was told yesterday the treatment has not been successful. Bonnie signed her own hospice admission paperwork. Jim was present. They have four adult children living in the area, although I have the impression they won't be very hands-on with her care."

The voice of the admission nurse was crisp and professional, but I could detect a note of attachment, protectiveness even, to this new patient and her plight. Our patients all have a prognosis of six months or less so we have to be on guard. Protectiveness and attachment can lead to heartbreak, and a heart broken too many times won't easily heal.

Yet, as I imagined the sad scene at the hospital yesterday, it was impossible to ignore the pain of a stranger named Jim watching his wife accept her prognosis with a signature. Allowing a fleeting moment of sadness, I then moved forward quickly to concentrate on what could be done for them. In hospice we reframe a perceived death sentence into a journey. My job is to guide our patients and families through the least understood portion of the trip.

With all my messages skimmed through and the blood in my body effectively replaced with coffee, I called in my schedule to Liz, our team secretary. *Today shouldn't be bad* I thought, quickly reading the names of the five patients I would visit.

With no disasters lurking, I pulled on a pair of dark slacks and a sweater topped by a lab coat. I smiled sincerely into the mirror as I put on some lipstick and combed my hair. Finally, I was ready to go out the door. As I picked up my ream of paperwork and my car keys, the phone rang. With my paperwork shifting and sliding precariously in my arms, I reached for the phone.

"Linda, you have an admission."

"Hi, Carol," I stammered in response. Carol's voice is distinctive, with a nasal northern quality to it, and often spoken in rapid fire, just like today. She is our team manager, with a dash of den mother thrown in.

"Yeah, good morning. So as I was saying, you have an admission."

"I just listened to voice mail."

"Then you heard the report."

"No, Carol. I only heard an admission for Marilyn."

"Yeah, that's the one. I need you to take her."

"But she lives by Marilyn, and I already have a full case load." I was whining like a two-year-old in need of a nap and didn't care.

"Right, but the patient, Bonnie, specifically asked for a nurse who would be honest with her. She was real nice on the phone, and when we finished talking I told her I had just the right nurse for her."

There was no rebuttal. Patients don't usually request a certain nurse unless they have met one of us while we were caring for a friend or family member. Bonnie hadn't actually asked for me, but in Carol's mind she had. I began redrawing my schedule for the day in my head as I wrote down Bonnie's address. "Seventeen patients, Carol, seventeen. Just remember that tomorrow when you want to give me another one."

"I know, I know. I'll leave you alone for now."

There was a smile in her voice, as she no doubt savored her victory. I could grumble and complain. I just couldn't work those feelings into anger toward Carol. She loved our patients too, and had the thankless job of sitting in the office managing all of us. I wasn't the only petulant child in the group who didn't always want to do as I was told.

With a final swig of cold coffee, I picked up my keys and paperwork again, causing the telephone to ring again.

"Hello?" I growled in my best what-the-hell-now tone of voice.

"Good morning, Sweets. How are you this morning?"

Kevin. With a deep sigh, I dropped my keys and paperwork on the table and myself into the nearest kitchen chair. His voice was halcyon, peaceful and reassuring, the antidote to Carol's call.

"Fine. At least I'm fine now. The morning has just been a little crazy." My what-the-hell tantrum had vanished at the sound of his voice.

"Is the cat okay?"

I felt a twinge of regret that I had caused him to be concerned over Twister.

"She's great. She ate. Then I shot her." It's okay to shoot her. She's diabetic and gets insulin twice every day.

"I just wanted to check on you this morning. I know it's a little bit lonely for you when I'm traveling, now that both kids are away at school."

"Lonely?" I asked. That thought hadn't crossed my mind. "I do miss them. Since they haven't called at least I know they're not out of money. Besides, I always picture them in class or in their dorm rooms studying, with their lights turned out by eleven. I have that active imagination to keep me company."

"So how is your morning going? Is it going to be a busy day?"

"Carol just gave me an admission that should have been Marilyn's. Oh, and I smelled perfume in the bedroom this morning while I was praying."

There was a pregnant pause. I wasn't worried, though. I have more faith in Kevin than in anyone else.

"I'm sorry you have another patient. But, who do you think was in the bedroom?" he asked.

"I don't know yet."

"I'm sure you'll figure it out," Kevin said simply, and I knew he meant it. "I hope you have a good day and don't have to work late. I just wanted to call to tell you I love you."

"I love you, too."

I replaced the receiver and gathered my keys and paperwork again. It's a wonderful gift to have someone who believes in you, even when you are not so sure of yourself.

CHAPTER 3

I never wanted to be a nurse. In my very wildest dreams I might have been the first woman astronaut orbiting the earth or fighting aliens on a distant planet while drinking powdered Tang in lieu of orange juice. I might have been a grocery clerk in charge of a cash register, responsibly ringing up groceries for housewives while making small talk about babies and politics. I might have even gone to a vocational school and achieved the ultimate goal of becoming a hairdresser, the profession long coveted by my mother.

Nursing, however, never crossed my mind. It happened completely by accident. Becoming a nurse at the time required white caps with black stripes, crisp starched uniforms, and higher education, and we weren't college people.

Mama worked in the factory making wiring harnesses for electric clothes dryers. The only time she wasn't working, she was walking a picket line. The reasons for the strikes varied with recurring themes of health care and better pay. All I thought about back then was that I couldn't join the Girl Scouts because it cost two dollars and we didn't have that kind of money to spare when the plant was on strike.

Daddy tended bar. This was after serving our country in the Pacific as a tail gunner on a B29, "the plane that won the war." His return home was greeted with appreciation, but without awareness or acknowledgment of the Post Traumatic Stress Disorder (PTSD) that would eventually take his life. He and my mother didn't live long enough to learn that they were the greatest generation.

Childhood bliss continued, apart from the occasional awareness of our finances, until I reached the age of seven. That is when I became acquainted with my share of doctors, nurses, and eventually undertakers. Hospitals and funeral parlors became part of my environment as relatives, most notably parents, got sick and died. As I grew so did the realization that I needed to support myself, which prompted me to spend an age-inappropriate amount of time pondering my future.

During my senior year in high school, I continued to contemplate the grocery clerk life. Rubbing elbows with doctors and nurses, however, had affected me more than I realized. My college-bound friends discussed potential careers, with many eliminating anything medical due to the gore factor. I had lived through much of that gore and felt comfortable pursuing something medical. Reading an article in *Seventeen Magazine,* a publication more often associated with lip gloss advice than career advice, clinched the decision and launched me on my way to the field of physical therapy.

I was sure physical therapy would be everything the paragraph in the magazine had promised. It had been only one of a multitude of careers showcased, so it hadn't really promised too much in fifty words or less. Undaunted by this minimal amount of information, I vowed to pursue my degree. My passion for physical therapy burned brightly for a semester. Then it was extinguished by love.

Since my new boyfriend attended a school that did not have a PT program, I found myself thumbing through the course catalog once again looking for something medical. This time I found nursing.

Before the shock of my decision had completely faded, I was called into the nursing school for my entrance interview. I sat on a metal folding chair across from an ancient woman, younger than I am now. She was wearing a polyester business suit and a whole can of hairspray. Her mouth turned up at the corners, forming her dark red lipstick into either a smirk or a smile. It was hard to tell.

"Did you always want to be a nurse, since you were a little girl?" she inquired.

"No, not really."

"Was your mother a nurse?" she persisted.

I suppose that question was so bizarre, I had difficulty knowing where to begin my answer. My mother had only finished ninth grade. Growing up in a family of nine children during the Great Depression, one of her accomplishments was not starving. She had to quit school because she didn't have shoes or school supplies. At the time, her family was dining, not infrequently, on the dandelion greens growing wild in their yard. Tuition for nursing school, or even vocational school to be a hairdresser, was not even a remote possibility. Mentally circling back to the question before me, I managed to whisper, "No."

"We have lots of students who follow their parents into the medical field. Perhaps your father, or maybe an uncle, was a doctor?"

If I hadn't been caught so off guard by this line of interrogation, I might have easily lied and said, "Mama was a doctor. Daddy was the nurse." Or I could have just spilled the dark truth and said, "My uncle was a pedophile, not a pediatrician."

However, by now I was beginning to panic that the right to enter nursing school was not based on my grade point and SAT scores, but inherited somehow. "Mama worked in the factory and Daddy was a bartender," I blurted out.

It was the irritable interviewer's turn to be stunned into silence. Looking at me from over the top of her half-moon reading glasses, she seemed to be trying to identify what biologic species sat before her. The scripted questions she had been reading obviously were not applicable in my case.

I had enough hard-earned confidence to meet her gaze and not blush. My fleeting moment of panic had passed. I reminded myself that it was in fact those grade point and test score numbers that had earned me the right to sit here in the first place. Waiting for her to speak, I breathed slowly and calmly. Nurses were cool and collected in a crisis, and I had had my share of crises far worse than an interview with Nurse Ratchet. Displaying serenity at a moment like this could win points, or I could have played my orphan card at this time and won the game. All I would need to say is, "My parents are deceased. I spent a great deal of time growing up around hospitals while they were ill. The compassion of the nurses I met led me to this calling."

Bullshit, however, is not my strong suit. I just sat on the metal folding chair, and smiled.

"Why are you here? Tell me what made you decide to be a nurse, in your own words." There was no longer a question of facial expressions at this point. She was returning my smile with a definite smirk as I edged closer to defiance.

"I need to support myself. Nurses can always get a job, and those jobs have benefits like medical insurance."

My mother had walked the picket line during all those union strikes to get decent pay and medical benefits. Those lessons weren't lost on me. I did at least have the presence of mind to omit the "following my boyfriend" portion of the story. The interviewer blinked and mumbled her dissatisfaction with my response. I was enrolling based on love, a magazine article, and instinct. The calling my interviewer wanted to discover would have to wait. I hadn't yet discovered it myself.

As anticipated, after graduation there were always jobs, first in Kentucky, then in Texas. I tried out many different nursing roles along the way and found I preferred the ones with the most patient contact. Management positions were just too similar to my early job experiences as a babysitter. Armed with this small amount of self-awareness, I was once again ready to make a change.

With a few copies of my resume in hand, I trekked to downtown Dallas to a medical job fair. Ignoring the many hospitals represented, I found myself circling the hospice booth. Drawn there by memories of some of my favorite oncology patients, I finally stepped forward.

"Hello, how may I help you? Are you interested in a team secretary position?" a tall pleasant woman asked.

"No, nothing administrative," I said. "I'm actually an RN."

This was not information to be shared easily. Being a nurse at a medical job fair is the equivalent of being Santa Claus at the mall. You are going to be surrounded, with everyone in the crowd hoping you will make their wishes come true. Instead of presents, however, they want staffing quotas met. In this case, the woman looked like she was about to kiss me instead of shaking my hand.

I left the job fair without talking to anyone else. The woman, who I now knew as Betsy, had imparted more information about hospice in our thirty-minute conversation than I thought was possible. Walking back to my car, I was certain I had a job offer coming, and equally certain I would accept it. The only information I could easily recall was the job description.

"Your job," Betsy said, "is to be a medically educated friend."

That had a warm fuzzy feel to it that I could not possibly resist.

CHAPTER 4

With my tidy, five patient schedule for the day effectively trashed by Carol's orders to take on a new admission, I pulled out my map and looked for yet another destination. As I had expected, Bonnie's home really was almost in Marilyn's backyard. The only comfort I could take at the moment was anticipating Marilyn's expression when she realized where Bonnie lived and that she was not her patient. Our mileage, as decreed by the Internal Revenue Service, begins when we leave our first patient's home. Starting her day so close to home would have been a bonus for Marilyn.

I took the back road from McKinney to Sachse and turned off just before Marilyn's neighborhood into a large mobile home park. It was February, but sunny and growing warm, trying hard to be April or May. I circled through the park, glancing at the lot numbers as my car crested each speed bump, searching for Bonnie's place. The homes were nestled on their narrow pie shaped lots in orderly fashion around the curving roads. Each had a parking pad in front with some cars and many pickup trucks glistening in the Texas sun. Trees were plentiful but still winter bare. Their scraggly limbs couldn't conceal the metal landscape composed of homes, vehicles, and garbage cans.

The overall picture was not unlike a military base with precision and functionality that stopped short of individuality. Bonnie and Jim's home was compliant with the others: a single-wide metal building, clean white in color, trimmed with a deep-sea blue. The steps and small porch matched the blue of the trim. I pulled onto a parking pad next to a pickup truck.

There's a moment before I meet each new patient that gives me pause. It's not exactly butterflies or nervousness, but it is related to that. There is a definite lump in my stomach. It's like the feeling when a police car pulls behind you. Everything will probably be fine. He's probably just headed in the same direction, but there is a fleeting moment looking in the rearview mirror of *What's next?*

Brushing aside any qualms, I gathered my phone, pager, and a pile of carbon copies, collectively known as an admission packet. Three wooden steps led up to the front porch. Some random pots sat in the corner, holding remnants of plants, now brown and dehydrated from neglect. Priorities. Plants are not very important to most men in the best of times, but especially not when their wives are dying.

Jim answered the door with a smile while his eyes glistened with held back tears. He was so tall he stooped slightly to open the storm door, giving the appearance of an adult in the doorway of a child's playhouse. His hair was thick and white, cropped short. Beside him, a stubby dog of questionable parentage gave a couple of non-threatening barks.

"Hush, Beau, get back," he said, nudging the scruffy dust mop of a dog away. Stepping back to let me enter, he automatically straightened to his full height, somewhere noticeably above six feet. He looked oddly familiar, until I realized General Waverly from the movie *White Christmas* could have been his identical twin brother.

The mobile homes I have visited have run the gamut from dangerous disrepair, such as holes in the floor covered with only carpet, to rampant roaches running everywhere, to designer decorated, ready for a magazine cover shot. The worst places I visit are the reason I carry spray bug repellent in my car. For those special circumstances, I spend a moment spritzing my shoes and the bottoms of my pant legs before each visit to keep out uninvited guests. Perhaps it's this wide range of unknown that creates some of that apprehension during a first visit.

This trailer had looked small from the outside and felt even smaller on the inside, especially standing next to Jim. I entered directly into the living room where I saw a chair and sofa framed with exposed slabs of wood forming the armrests and legs. Faded plaid upholstery, in lifeless hues of reds, blues, and tans, covered thick cushions on each piece. A little television sat in the corner. The kitchen, which opened to the living room on my right, was just as utilitarian.

Formica counters, once white but now faded out to gray in several large spots, ran the perimeter. A white refrigerator and stove were the only appliances except for a toaster and a coffee pot on the worn counter. A dish drainer was barely visible next to the sink, a clean dishtowel thrown over its contents, concealing the only evidence that the kitchen had been used today. The air revealed no stale cooking smells, or other unpleasant odors, or perfume for that matter. If spotless was a scent, that was what I smelled. Mentally, I was checking boxes on the admission form I carried: no dangerous animals, no unsanitary conditions, a safe environment.

The General, as I now thought of him, led me quietly through the living area, away from the kitchen, and down a narrow hall on the other side. The first door off the hall led to a small, wood-paneled bedroom. The room was completely filled with a bed in front of the window and a dresser pushed against one wall. Like the living room and kitchen, it was a functional space, unadorned by mementoes that would be expected after a long marriage.

A wisp of a woman appeared from piles of pillows and blankets, propping herself up on her elbows as I entered. A frown flashed across her face with the effort, which she hid quickly. She was painfully thin, her body ravaged equally by the disease and the treatment. Sparse, random tufts of hair sprung from her near naked scalp at odd angles. She reached up to brush them down with her hand, most likely a leftover habit from having a full head of hair to run her fingers through. With eyes that looked into my heart and a firm handshake, she greeted me, "Hello, I'm Bonnie."

"Linda," I replied, holding her hand in mine as I met her gaze. She was looking at me, but also through me. It felt like I could say whatever I wanted. She would discern the truth with her eyes.

"I asked your manager for a nurse who would always be honest with me, and she sent you. Did Carol listen to me? Did she send the right person?" Her voice was steady. Unlike Jim, Bonnie had already packed away yesterday's tears.

Pausing a second to collect my thoughts, I decided to give the long answer to her question. "When I was still a child, my mother had cancer. Her doctors lied to her. They never told her she was dying. By the time she realized the truth, she was too sick to make any plans for me. I really hate it when medical people lie. It is, after all, your body and your life."

"That's a tough way to learn the value of honesty. It sounds like I found my nurse." She was smiling as she spoke, but in her unfaltering gaze I saw trust.

Jim filled the bedroom doorway. The look on his face said he'd like to be somewhere, anywhere, else. "Do you mind if I run to the store? Do you need me for anything?"

"We'll be fine," I assured him. Patting my thick pile of paperwork I added, "We'll be busy for quite a while."

Looking back at Bonnie, I knew we would be fine. With effort, I forced myself to think ahead to the last visit I might make to Bonnie. I turned away for a second, shuffling through my papers to find page one, while also trying to picture what it would be like to pronounce her as deceased. It's a ghastly and morbid thought, but I have to focus on the fact that I am meeting a hospice patient, not just a new friend. Bonnie and I were going to be friends anyway. There might just have to be some heartbreak this time.

"Thanks," Jim answered, smiling at Bonnie. "She's fine. I just get a little nervous leaving her alone. We're absolutely out of everything. I haven't been to the store in a couple of weeks since she went back into the hospital this last time."

"Get going or we're going to starve," Bonnie said with more playfulness than she probably felt. "And take your time. We have a lot to talk about," she finished, indicating my pile of paperwork.

As soon as she heard Jim close the front door behind him, Bonnie let herself fall back on her pile of pillows. She was weak, already on the edge of bedbound. Without emphasizing that fact, we decided to order a hospital bed and set it up in the living room. This would put her in the heart of the little house. From there she could supervise Jim's attempted cooking in the nearby kitchen, watch television, or more and more often, just nap.

"Jim seems like a wonderful guy. It's not always easy for men to be caregivers, so I am impressed at his willingness to go to the store."

"Well, I've been sick for a couple of years, and during that time he came to the realization that grocery stores are critical to eating." Bonnie had turned on her side and propped her head in her hand. She smiled as she talked about Jim.

"How long have you been married?"

"We met over forty years ago and didn't really wait any time to get married. We were both just kids. He had just joined the military and it all seemed like such an adventure. I didn't realize that I was pledging my love to one man, and my allegiance to the entire armed services. When they said go, we did, kids and all. Of course, the promise of travel to exotic lands included more packing paper and chipped dishes than suitcases and suntan lotion."

"And you wouldn't have traded a minute of it," I added.

"No, I wouldn't have done anything differently. Home was whatever base the army said it was. Then when we, I mean Jim, retired we had to decide where we wanted to live for a change."

"And how did you decide to come here?"

"This isn't where we retired. We bought a big sprawling house, rockers on the porch, the works. We chose Texas because that's where the children, and more importantly the grandchildren, ended up. This trailer came later."

"Oh," I said not wanting to pry, stifling my curiosity about the destiny of the sprawling ranch house.

"When you live in base housing, you miss a few things. I suppose the main thing we longed for was space, the kind of space where you look out your front door or back door and own what you see. No other houses or neighbors in your line of sight. So that's what we bought. It was everything we imagined. The grandchildren would often come stay. Free babysitting is always in demand."

"I could have used some of that myself when mine were growing up! They would have loved staying out in the country," I said as I glanced at my watch to count her pulse.

"How many children do you have?" she asked.

Discussing our personal lives with patients is considered unprofessional, so as I finished my fifteen-second count, I said, "Two, a son named Andrew and a daughter named Nicole. They are grown now, or at least they think they are. Both are away at college so we're empty nesters, at least until summer." Professional and personal are just not mutually exclusive concepts to me.

She smiled broadly as the topic turned to children, the favorite topic of most mothers. "We have four children and a gaggle of grandkids. And yes, they did love visiting us in the country. Once I got sick it just wasn't that hard to give it up. We decided it would be easier to sell it and move closer to the doctors and hospitals. Living in the country is a lot more fun when you can make leisurely trips to town than when you have to go to chemotherapy appointments. And Jim is so practical. Getting a mobile home required much less care than our big house and acreage. Jim's plan was to buy another house somewhere as soon as this war was won."

"What were your plans?"

"Hmmm. You're observant. I like that. I knew we weren't going to win," Bonnie paused, as if she needed to digest the statement she had just made. "I don't think I've ever said that aloud. It sounds like I gave up, and that wasn't the case at all. It's just something I felt inside. I tried every treatment the doctors dreamed up, and sometimes they, the treatments and the doctors, were real nightmares. I don't know how to describe it, except knowing the outcome was more like a gift. Feeling the cancer was terminal made it less devastating when the oncologist finally figured it out."

"Yesterday."

"Yesterday is when they told us. I think the doctors suspected it all along. In a single conversation I went from being a cancer patient to a hospice patient. For Jim, of course, well…"

"He loves you and he is not ready to lose you. A big part of my job is preparing Jim for what is to come. Your job, on the other hand, is to lie in this new bed we're ordering for you, and give commands."

"All I have enough energy for is telling everyone else what they should be doing. And don't worry about convincing Jim there is a heaven. We're believers. It just doesn't make it that much easier for him to be left behind."

"Bonnie, the way I see it, you are not actually leaving him behind."

The look in Bonnie's eyes clearly spoke her disbelief. "Six months or less. That's what they said, and personally, I believe 'less' is the key word."

"I think you're right about the time. Six months just seems to be the magical number the doctors all pull from thin air. Maybe half of a year sounds like enough time to get something done. I'm not sure. I just meant that heaven might not be somewhere else. It might be right here."

"No fluffy clouds?"

"Sorry, I don't think so. God probably doesn't have a beard either, unless you end up in a Renaissance painting."

She looked like a mischievous imp, sitting up in bed, knees bent, with her thin arms wrapped around them. She was grinning now, which told me there were no accusations of blasphemy in the air. "So the doctor pulled the six month number out of his butt and I'm not getting a harp, halo, or wings."

I smiled back at her. She might end up breaking my heart, but she would be a heck of a lot of fun in the meantime. "The streets of heaven are probably not paved with gold either."

"Damn. You aren't going to let me have anything to look forward to. And here I thought my riches were stored in heaven. That's what all the preachers tell you, especially when they're asking for money."

"Since I haven't actually been there myself, I can't guarantee anything. Maybe you will get the Michelangelo version of heaven…"

"No streets of gold, no wings, and no TV evangelist prophesies coming true. I get all that. We've gone over what heaven isn't." Bonnie was looking me straight in the eye, holding me with her gaze. Her smile was fading into concern. For all her courage in the face of the truth she had been handed, she had her share of fears hovering just beneath the bravado. "I'm asking what happens next. Instead of more talk about what heaven isn't, I want to hear what you think heaven is like.

Apparently, I'll be there soon, and I need to know what to pack for the trip."

I was sitting on the edge of her bed, just as my nursing instructors had told me to never do, preparing to discuss spiritual beliefs without a single theology class to my credit. I remembered talking with Betsy from the hospice booth at the job fair. She had said my job description was to be "a medically educated friend." That was the only instruction I was following at the moment.

"I definitely believe in life after death, a version of heaven. I couldn't do this job if I thought life came crashing to an end with death. I'm not sure how I would even get up in the morning, for that matter, if I didn't believe." I chewed on my lip and prayed for the right words to come. I wanted to shed whatever light I could on the unknown, dispersing those shadowy fears.

Patting her hand, I said, "I guess physicists would talk about matter and energy not being created or destroyed. Preachers would talk about the harps and halos. I'm a hospice nurse, so my frame of reference is what my patients and their families have experienced. Like I was saying, I haven't been there, so I'm not trying to tell you that I have it all figured out. I wish I did. However, I have been close to a number of people at the end, and those experiences are providing a few pieces to the puzzle. And this puzzle repeatedly takes the same shape regardless of my patients' religious beliefs or often, lack of beliefs altogether."

I couldn't give her the whole picture because I didn't have it. The most I could do was supply some of those puzzle pieces. As she assembled them, her own picture would emerge.

"I had a patient a year or so ago named Manuel who fought in the South Pacific in World War II. He told me that walking became more frightening than fighting the Japanese during the war. Waving a gnarled finger in the air he said the enemy was no longer 'out there'; now the enemy was the cancer inside him. He and his wife were struggling to maintain their home and independence, so at first he used a cane, then a walker. When he could no longer walk at all, I knew he would pass away quickly, and he did."

"I know a little about how he felt," Bonnie said. "I don't feel like I'm ready to go yet, but I never imagined how it would feel to no longer walk, at least not until about a week ago."

"Moving you around is easy for Jim, even if it's humbling for you. For Manuel's petite wife Maria, it was impossible. She was terrified of either of them being placed in a nursing home, and if he couldn't get out of bed that was bound to happen. He couldn't put her through that so instead he passed away."

"People have that kind of control? When he couldn't walk, he died?" Bonnie asked.

"He was bedbound, still at home, for a couple of days.

Then he died. Letting go seems to be more of an active decision than a passive event."

Bonnie fell silent, her brow furrowed. For a woman who had so recently lost the ability to walk, having control over anything, especially the time of her own death, seemed to be food for thought.

"I went to the funeral and was invited back to the house with the family afterward. We were standing around, talking about Manuel, when his four-year-old great-grandson ran out of the bedroom. He pulled and tugged on the adults, making enough ruckus to stop the conversation and get everyone's attention. With his hands on his hips he announced that he had just seen his grandfather. Pointing to the bedroom where Manuel had died, he said, 'I just saw Grandpa in there. He can walk again, and he's smiling.'"

There was a comfortable silence between Bonnie and me. Turning my attention to my paperwork, I wanted to give Bonnie time to think. While I checked boxes and made brief notes, she sat quietly, absentmindedly rubbing those random tufts of hair as she thought about what I had said. She might not agree with my ideas about heaven, or even believe Manuel's story for that matter; however, Bonnie had professed to want the truth. This was just one of many truths experienced by patients and families, and sometimes their nurse. Manuel's grandson had seen him walking and smiling. How many families have similar, inexplicable stories? Too often they get brushed away, labeled as dreams or irrational thoughts instead of valued as the gift they are.

"Children don't lie, at least not about something like that," she finally said.

"No, I don't think they do."

"I'm guessing what happened with Manuel isn't an isolated event."

"No," I answered, thinking of the mysterious perfume in my bedroom from this morning. "Not at all."

"Hmm," she said. "So you think this is what happens. I'll be able to walk again, have my strength back."

"Not with this body, but yes. Somehow, some way that is beyond my understanding, you will go on."

"You said you lost your mom as a child."

"And my dad."

"Is that why you do this job?"

"Yes. I hadn't thought it through until one day our team chaplain Tom explained it. He said, 'We minister out of our own pain.'"

In her eyes I saw understanding rather than pity or curiosity. She understood how I came to be sitting on the edge of her bed, holding her hand, telling her miraculous stories. I had thumbed through a magazine and found something medical. I had looked for job security and benefits. Introspection had had to wait. Hospice nursing now felt like my calling, but the call had been slow in coming. It arrived like the tinkle of a wind chime rather than the clanging of a bell.

CHAPTER 5

November 1967

The first moan I heard from Daddy stopped me in my tracks. When I heard him cry out in pain, my heart broke. I had heard people talk about a broken heart, now I understood what it meant.

Running up the steps and across the porch that afternoon, I couldn't wait to leave the spitting sky and cold wind behind. If Sister Mary James asked me to draw a picture of Kentucky in the winter, I'd only need a white piece of paper and a gray crayon. The sky stays gray. Sleet and snow are white. There aren't any other colors.

I turned the knob of the big oak door, and with a single

step was wrapped in warmth provided by the gas furnace. Almost immediately, my legs began to sting, thawing in the sudden heat. That's when the sounds first struck me from the next room.

Our house isn't large enough for fancy things the other kids at school have, like entryways or halls. The front door opens straight into the living room, with the French doors to my parents' room immediately to the right. Their room used to be a dining room. Mama said that was an awful waste in a house with just one bedroom. By putting the dining table in the basement and moving a full-size bed and dresser into the dining room, she had doubled the number of bedrooms from one to two.

Today, for the first time ever during the day, the French doors were closed. Whispers and moans snaked through the curtained glass. My stomach hurt. "Mama? Daddy? Nina? Can I come in?" I tried to open the door, but somebody held the knob from the other side.

"Not now," Nina said. My grandmother never says no to me.

"I want to see my daddy!"

"No, you need to pray for him. God answers the prayers of children and your daddy needs your prayers now."

I didn't understand why Daddy was making these sounds. He's brave and strong. His picture is even in a book we have about the Pacific battles in World War II, so I know he's brave. I've never seen him cry or even look scared. I tried to think about the photos of him in his uniform, young and smiling. The sounds coming from the bedroom made that hard.

With nothing to do except worry, I stretched out on the living room floor to watch cartoons. No one told me to stop watching and eat dinner. No one said I should take a break from television to go play. Now with the room getting darker, my eyes looked at the black and white flicker of the screen, while my ears stayed tuned to the sounds still coming from the next room.

"He has to go the hospital," Mama said just about every time Daddy made a sound. "You have to help me convince him."

"I know, but he won't go," Nina whispered back in a scared, shaky voice I'd never heard from her before.

The darkness made me more afraid, or the sounds louder, or both. My bed is the pullout couch in the living room, a space I share with Nina. Tonight I had all the lumps and bumps of the mattress to myself. Nina and Mama whispered in the next room. Daddy was there, the sound of his pain still hurting my heart. Nina's pillow over my ears didn't keep those noises out of my head. With the television turned off, there was nothing else to listen to.

"Our Father, who art in heaven, please make Daddy well." I prayed and I cried and somehow, eventually fell asleep.

Walking home from school the next day, I worried. For the first time in my seven years, I didn't know what to expect. I opened the door slowly, more aware of the butterflies in my stomach than my frozen stick legs. The French doors were swung open wide in their usual position, the bed was neatly made, and soft winter sunlight streamed in through the sheer curtains. Yesterday might never have happened. The butterflies left for a minute as I realized Daddy wasn't here. Then they flew right back as I wondered aloud, "Where did he go?

Nina abandoned her big pile of ironing to hold me. We sat in her stuffed chair as she talked of doctors and hospitals and Daddy getting well. Breathing in the scent of her talcum powder, cradled in her plump arms, the butterflies fluttered slowly away again.

"He'll be fine," she repeated once or twice too often to be believed. "Ain't he just a young man? Ain't he practically a boy?"

No, he isn't, I thought to myself. He was a daddy, and fathers are old, just not as old as Nina. My ain'ts had already been replaced by isn'ts thanks to the Holy Sisters of Perpetual Punishment. The meaning was the same.

Life fell into a new routine as we waited for Daddy to come back home. Mama worked days and sat at the hospital at night. Nina and I ate dinner alone. Only my sister was the same. She stayed in her bedroom, the only real bedroom in the entire house, stretched out, studying, on one of the two twin beds.

Her books stretched across the other bed. It was one of life's great mysteries that her college books got a twin bed of their own when Nina and I had to share a lumpy pullout couch. Still, she was the only person any of us knew on a first name basis who had gone to college. I wondered if when she graduated in a year or so, that first name basis would become a thing of the past. Knowing my sister, she would probably make all of us call her "Madam" or "Your Royal Highness" or something.

As our wait continued, the word *stroke* floated about in the air, usually when neighbors or relatives stopped by. I didn't know what a stroke was, but it was terrible. It was sickness so terrible, in fact, a person with it had to go to the hospital. I didn't know if I could catch it like a cold or not. I didn't really care. I just wanted my daddy. The hospital wouldn't even let me visit because I was too young.

Just before my birthday, Daddy finally came home. There wasn't any money for birthday presents because Daddy hadn't worked in so long. I didn't care. I just wanted Daddy. He had other ideas, though. He gave up his prized silver dollars along with his Kennedy half-dollars to buy a Timex wristwatch for me.

CHAPTER 6

The predominant season in Texas is summer. It's hot with some wind and Crayola blue skies disturbed only by an occasional puff of white cloud. Summer occupies the traditional months of June, July, and August. It also sprinkles a few of its hot days at random into the other months. February catches one of them here and there, but yesterday's warmth was now only a memory. Today dawned cold, steel gray, with the crisp smell of frost back in the air, and not a trace of perfume in my bedroom or anywhere else.

My office on wheels is in the form of a Volkswagen. Before backing out of the garage, I loaded up the yellow Beetle with a fresh stack of forms and a few extra supplies, shivering in my lab coat as I arranged everything. I hate the cold, just not as much as I hate a winter coat. As my neighbor says, my yellow Bug looks like a big lemon driving down the road, but at least it's a lemon with heated seats. I flipped the switch on the seat heater and double-checked the passenger seat for my stethoscope and blood pressure cuff, then headed north.

The roads to the north of McKinney are lightly traveled. Around here, driving to McKinney is called "going to town" and going to Dallas is unheard of. Two-lane blacktop ribbons wind through this part of Collin County with some unpaved local roads shooting off at intervals. Pickup trucks seem to greatly outnumber cars. So do cows. The pickup drivers usually wave or give a nod of the head as we pass, so I make it a habit to drive with my left hand at the top of the steering wheel, an automatic wave at the ready. A lack of traffic, friendly drivers, and a view of rolling hills are my rewards for visiting patients in outlying areas.

Since the beginning of last week, I have been making a daily trek into the countryside to visit an elfin patient sweetly and appropriately named Grace. As I wind my way north toward her home, I wonder how Grace can still be with us. Unlike Bonnie, who will be receiving one nursing visit and a few home health aide visits each week, Grace is imminent and receiving around-the-clock care. We call this private duty attention Continuous Care, and usually only provide it for a very few days. When I started working for hospice we had called it Crisis Care, then changed the name because I suppose someone realized being on hospice is already a crisis, certainly for the family if not the patient. Grace, however, is now well into her second week of Continuous Care. Patients on this level of care receive registered nurse visits every day.

Continuous Care patients have a home health aide during the day, while at night a licensed vocational nurse takes over. Grace is blessed to be cared for during the day, at least most days, by Twilla, one of my favorite home health aides. Twilla is an old soul in a young package. She has a ready and warm smile, and equally ready tears. Her skin is the color of midnight and she has deep dark eyes to match, eyes that sparkle when she talks about either her son or her current patient. Twilla is strong, yet exudes a strength that has as much to do with her spirit as with her physical attributes. I find myself seeking her opinion and even her approval. She is one of my hospice mentors.

Twilla's job is much more challenging than mine, a fact I willingly admit. She stays with the dying or distressed patient all day, every day. She bathes the patient, turns them, feeds them if they are able to eat, and if not, hugs the family tight while she explains why Mom or Dad can't swallow anymore. By comparison, my role as the hospice nurse is to visit for an hour or so. Besides generating mounds of paperwork, I provide a physical assessment, family teaching, and call the doctor, changing medications and orders as directed. I love my patients and most of their families, but I'm glad I don't have Twilla's job.

Twilla was off yesterday, so I was anxious to see both her and Grace. I made Grace's sparse little farmhouse my first stop. The house had been closed up and emptied out, devoid of furnishings and inhabitants for years. When Grace was sent home from the hospital to pass away, as the doctors had delicately phrased it, her daughter Penny took them at their word. Grace had spent her recent years in a sparkling clean brick and stucco nursing home, which had never really been home. This shabby little house with the slightly sagging porch was her true home. So, this is where Penny brought her mother to die. The only furnishings were Penny's army-style cot in the second bedroom, and in Grace's room, a hospital bed and oxygen sent by hospice, and two comfortable chairs Penny had thoughtfully provided for us, the staff.

Twilla was turning her patient and fluffing pillows as I arrived. "She's not ready yet," Twilla commented as I entered the room, acknowledging my arrival without looking away from her patient. "She's still waiting for something."

"I think you're right," I said, situating my clipboard and other paraphernalia in the windowsill. I grabbed the blood pressure cuff and turned toward Twilla and Grace. "I just wish I knew who or what she is waiting for. Besides her children, most of her family and friends are gone. Penny is here nearly all the time, and both sons stop by every day. How was she last night? Did the night nurse notice any changes?"

"She said she seemed about the same. I don't really see any changes in her myself since I was off yesterday."

"Well, I know you have to have a day off, but I'm glad to have you back with Grace." As I spoke, the sound of Grace's raspy little breaths could be heard in reply from across the room.

"Hi, Grace. It's Linda. I'll bet you're happy to have Twilla back today taking care of you. We won't tell her what a great job she does. That would just go to her head." Twilla grinned at me with a trace of a blush crossing her cheeks.

I warmed my stethoscope in both hands. "Grace, this may still be a bit chilly. Hopefully it won't be terrible."

I placed my stethoscope against Grace's chest with my right hand while resting my left hand on her shoulder. Listening to the rapid, fluttering beat of her heart, I wondered how much longer it could go on. Her breathing was diminished, too. It was hard to tell what was keeping her alive. It certainly didn't seem to be oxygen when she was getting so little. "Her breathing is still really rough. I'm guessing she's having periods of apnea."

Apnea is irregular breathing. There are moments when it seems the next breath might never come. It is common for actively dying patients to have this very irregular breathing, and frightening for the family. Sometimes patients don't breathe for a minute or so, almost as if they are deciding whether or not to take the next breath.

Twilla nodded. "She is having apnea, but she only has it for about ten, maybe fifteen seconds at a time."

"Grace, I'm just checking your tummy now. It won't hurt, I promise."

I listened for the normal rumbling of bowel sounds with my stethoscope, but heard none. As gently as possible, I palpated her abdomen. Twilla stood across from me on the other side of the bed, ready to assist if I needed it, but more importantly to hear how her beloved patient was doing. Tucking the quilts back around her upper body, I then pulled back the covers from the bottom of the bed on my side to check Grace's feet. Twilla did the same on her side.

"Her feet are cold," Twilla commented. "There is no way to get them warm."

"No, there's not. These quilts are plenty, and they're soft. I love old quilts like these that feel like they've been washed and hung out on the clothesline to dry a hundred times over the years. Don't worry. You're keeping her warm enough." Twilla knew what to expect, and decreasing circulation was a given. Sitting here for eleven or twelve hours each day cost her a bit of perspective. She needed reassurance just like families do.

Once my head-to-toe assessment was complete, I grabbed my clipboard and three-page form, and flopped into the chair.

Twilla tucked Grace's feet back under the covers to her own satisfaction and took the other seat.

"How's your son doing, Twilla?" I asked after writing Grace's name and identification number across the top of the first page.

"He's fine. It was really nice to be home with him yesterday, although I missed Grace. I cleaned house all day while he was at school, making sure I was through by the time he got off the bus in the afternoon. I cooked supper and we had a nice relaxing evening together."

They live on the south side of Dallas in an area that Twilla has often said makes it difficult to raise a good child. While my biggest worries in recent years had been about SAT scores, class rankings, and college acceptance letters for Andrew and Nicole, Twilla worries about protecting her son from crime and crack houses and gangs. There is crime in my world as well, just not the home invasion and drive-by shooting variety that Twilla lives with.

"I wondered if Grace would pass while I was gone."

"No, I have a feeling she'll want you here when she goes," I said without looking up as I made quick check marks in the appropriate blocks and added brief comments on the first page of my nurse's notes.

"I think she might," Twilla added.

Grace might not be able to speak or communicate with us

in any other way, yet I knew she was still inside that frail little body. That meant she knew who was with her, what was being said to her, and about her. With that in mind, what more could anyone ask than to pass away in Twilla's loving care?

We sat in companionable silence while I finished my paperwork. The room felt warm, almost cozy, in spite of the lack of furnishings and the weak winter light filtering in through the dusty windowpane. The hospital bed with its faded quilts and the two chairs nearly filled the small space. With the tasks at hand completed, I was reluctant to leave Grace and her little room. It was hard to tear myself away and face the bleak winter day waiting outside. Besides, there was every chance I would never be back. Grace couldn't hang on much longer.

"I didn't tell you what happened to me yesterday," I said, grasping for a reason to linger. Also, Twilla was one of the few people, like Kevin, who could be trusted with such a bizarre experience. I knew Twilla would accept the situation and possibly even shed some light on the cause. "It was the strangest thing. I was just getting up for work when I smelled perfume in my bedroom, and I can't figure it out. I was praying when quite suddenly the scent was just floating around me. It was definitely perfume, but not a fragrance I recognized. It was there for a few minutes, and then just as suddenly as it arrived, it vanished. It doesn't make any sense. There's nothing scented at all in my bedroom."

I had put my pen away and was rubbing Grace's tiny hand as I talked, listening to her raspy breathing. When I looked up, Twilla was staring at me from across the bed. Her back was rod straight, her eyes wide, her ebony skin paled.

"That's happened to me," she whispered.

"When?"

"I don't remember. I just know I have smelled someone's perfume when I was alone."

"When?" I persisted, forcing myself to wait for her to speak. I had to hear her say it.

Across the bed, her eyes met mine. Tension sparked in the air. We both knew what was about to unfold. All that remained was for her to say it out loud.

"I don't remember, I'm just saying those things can happen…"

"Twilla, tell me."

"It was three o'clock this morning. The perfume woke me up and I couldn't go back to sleep."

"My gosh!" I said, lost for words.

We were quiet for a few moments as we each processed our shared experience. Luckily, Penny was not in her mother's room at the time, so when we found words to discuss our perfume experiences only Grace was present. She was comatose, but likely listening.

"Do you think it was Jane?" Twilla asked.

The last patient we saw together was an elegant lady named Jane who passed away the day after Christmas. She was a lady who would have had a signature fragrance. Her daughter played the piano in an impeccably decorated home so her mother could pass away in comfort, listening to her favorite music. Jane was the probable wearer of perfume.

"That's not it," I said after much discussion. "I only saw Jane once, on the day she died. It was a long visit, but I don't believe it could have been her. Jane was Marilyn's patient, not mine, and that was the only time I saw her. I really didn't know her."

"We live at least forty miles apart, yet we both smelled perfume at home. How can that be?" Twilla asked. "There has to be a reason."

"I know. I can't imagine what it could be. Jane is gone and certainly doesn't need perfume now."

"It almost had to be Jane," Twilla insisted. "You and I haven't had that many patients together this winter. Let's turn Grace on her side. She doesn't look comfortable to me."

Standing on the opposite side of the bed, I helped Twilla remove the pillows around Grace in preparation for repositioning her. Grace weighed almost nothing so Twilla could do this by herself. However, with the two of us turning her together it could be done seamlessly. As we worked I added, "I just don't know why we would be smelling her perfume, or anyone else's for that matter."

Penny walked in the room as we finished turning her mother, and our conversation concluded in a perfect circle. "It had to be Jane's perfume... It couldn't be Jane's perfume."

"Did your mom wear perfume?" I asked Penny.

She looked startled but this was week two of my daily visits and accompanying odd comments, so she just answered the question. "White Shoulders. She always wore it, always. People used to remark on it all the time. They said it smelled better on her than anyone. Perfume is like that. A perfume smells different on different people."

Twilla sat back down with a thump.

"Can you get it?" I asked Penny, looking around the bare room hopefully. "Do you have some here?"

"I have a bottle down the way at my house. I was going back this morning to get the clean sheets to change Mom's bed. I could bring it back with me then."

Like Twilla, with an unceremonious plop I landed in the other chair, unable to stand. "I'll wait." I knew my next four patients were stable and besides, I needed to smell White Shoulders and I needed to smell it on Grace.

"Do you think it's really Grace's perfume we smelled?" Twilla asked when Penny left the room.

I shook my head and sighed. "I guess it could be, if it was that important to Grace to wear her White Shoulders every day. I just still feel confused about the whole thing."

"Just because we don't understand it and can't explain it doesn't make it any less real," Twilla said.

Penny reappeared in moments. "I sent my brother to fetch Mom's perfume and the clean sheets. I told him we needed them in a hurry and he was too afraid to ask why. I'm sure he thought it was the sheets we were anxious to get." She tossed a pile of folded linen on the foot of the bed after pulling out the bottle of perfume tucked safely in the stack. "You told me the sense of smell stays, just like hearing, as people are dying. Do you really think Mom wants her perfume?"

"Twilla and I both smelled perfume out of the blue in our bedrooms and don't know why. I smelled it yesterday and she smelled it today."

"That does seem a bit odd," Penny said.

"Trust me, Penny. This is strange even for us," I said with Twilla nodding in agreement.

"Mom never did go anywhere without her perfume. She never had fancy clothes or much makeup, but she had her perfume," she said as she uncapped the bottle. Spraying her hands with White Shoulders, she rubbed the scent on Grace. Twilla smelled it first and left the room crying while I just nodded my head. My legs wouldn't carry me out of the room. Grace's breathing quieted, even as I breathed in the exact fragrance that had visited my bedroom.

CHAPTER 7

Wednesday dawns earlier than the rest of the week. This Wednesday was no different than most. Out of bed at the crack of dark, I began preparing for my weekly journey to Dallas. Our hospice, inspired by the Medicare guidelines, invites us to the office for a mandatory weekly meeting. For one day of the week, I am not flying solo, connected to other team members only by tenuous electronic communication.

"You're up early." Kevin was back from his trip and mumbling from beneath the covers as I opened the bathroom door, billowing a cloud of soap-scented steam.

"Wednesday," I answered on my way to the closet.

"When will you be home?"

"Hmm, I don't really know. I'm pretty caught up with my

visits this week, so I guess that means I'll get an admission. It really depends on if any of the nurses need help, or if Carol thinks of something I need to do after team meeting."

"Tell them you need to come home early and have a relaxing evening."

"I'll tell them I've been neglecting you and need to get home to cook dinner," I answered, leaning over for a quick kiss before dashing toward the bedroom door. "Coffee's ready. I'm taking mine to go. Love you."

"I love you, too. Be careful," Kevin called after me.

This morning was starting the same as most mornings. On my way out the door, I paused for a second at the freezer and took out some meat in anticipation of cooking a scrumptious romantic dinner. I pictured myself home at a reasonable time, standing at the counter leisurely chopping fresh herbs and vegetables. In this daydream, the table is set, possibly with china. Candles are burning and the flowers on the table are fresh, not two weeks old from the grocery store.

In reality, I probably won't be home on time. I will be holding my cell phone in one hand the entire time I am cooking. On good nights, it has enough of a battery charge that I can move about freely, not tethered to an electrical cord. I will be on hold with the pharmacy. I always am. In between trying to get medications called in, I will be returning calls to families that came in during the day while I was with another patient. Simultaneously, I'll be tossing clothes in the washer all while not catching myself on fire at the stove or slicing my hand off with a knife.

Any lingering optimism blew out the car window this morning as I shifted the Bug into fourth gear to merge onto the highway, only to downshift back to second. The radio announcer confirmed that I had driven into a parking lot that had previously been a highway. "There's an accident southbound on the Dallas North Tollway coming into Dallas, on Central Expressway there's a stalled car in the HOV lane at Parker Road…"

As the recitation of delays continued belly dancing music began playing in my car. Fumbling in the cup holder, I reached for my phone. Kevin set belly dancing music as my ring tone to be funny. I don't know how to change it, and I'm not sure I would, though I will never tell him that.

"Hi, Angela! Where are you?" I said after a quick glance at Caller ID. Angela had been a hospice nurse for nearly three months when I started the job. With the rampant turnover in hospice that meant she was deemed experienced enough to train me. We had been friends ever since, with shared memories of starched white dresses, white stockings, and matching white caps bobby pinned painfully in our hair.

"I'm in Plano and guessing you're stuck in this traffic nightmare too," she answered with exasperation.

"I'm barely rolling forward. So, how have you been?" With that Angela and I settled into another long chat to fight off commuters' coma.

Angela and I share a bond much more important than the era in which we attended nursing school or the fact we work for the same hospice company. Angela and Mama have the same birthday. The year is much different of course, but the month and day are the same. When a loved one dies their birthday transforms immediately from a celebration of cake, cards, and presents to just another Tuesday or Wednesday. The person who died took the special with them.

Thanks to Angela, as Mama's birthday approaches every year, I get to celebrate. The date is once again elevated from an ordinary day of the week. Even the small act of buying a birthday card brings a measure of happiness. This would only sound insignificant to someone who still has their heart intact, unscarred by the loss of family and friends.

All holidays after a death are emotional milestones. Christmas gets a number, becoming the first or second or third Christmas without a spouse or parent. My first holidays after Mama's death were Thanksgiving and my birthday. They happened the month she died, rendering both of them indistinct, part of the swirl of grief. Besides, at the time I had much bigger worries than a turkey dinner and turning thirteen.

Christmas was the first holiday lightly penciled in on my

calendar. I marked it by venturing up in the attic and dragging down our shiny aluminum tree and matching color wheel. It wasn't a celebration, but lying on the floor watching the metallic branches shimmer in alternating patterns of red, blue and green I thought about happier Christmases gone by. Then I cried.

In just under two hours, I was walking through the door of the office conference room, memories of traffic and childhood swept aside. I shivered as the frosty air hit me, air the exact same temperature as a walk-in cooler. This one room of our office is always uncomfortably cold. Something seems to be mysteriously wrong with the thermostat. It is stuck in "goose bumps to keep meeting attendees awake" mode.

Folding tables were pushed together to run the length of the room. At the far end in front of floor-to-ceiling windows, the home health aides started taking their seats like naughty children at the back of the classroom. Technically, they come to team meeting to contribute information about the patients. In reality, they are here to visit with each other and catch up on the week's events.

"Hey, sweetie!"

"Tricia! I didn't hear you come up behind me," I said, shifting my paperwork to one arm so I could get a hug.

"That's not surprising. It's noisy in here," Tricia said with a smile. As our team social worker she comes equipped with smiles, hugs, and tissues.

On cue, Carol blew in the door. "Take your seats, everybody, so we can get started. Dr. Kazi is on his way. Here are the agendas. Nurses, don't forget to turn in your infection reports and any incident reports you have on patient falls. I don't care so much if you do them or not, but I am getting tired of getting yelled at by the higher ups for not having everything turned in."

Her instructions were brisk and breathless, hurried like everything about her. As she spoke she began passing out piles of paperwork: medication sheets for the nurses and agendas to the staff. She was pencil thin, probably because fat couldn't catch her. Her feathery red hair bobbed in the breeze her rapid movements created.

"It's amazing that she doesn't run out of breath," I whispered, taking a seat across from Tricia.

"I just want some of her energy," Tricia answered.

"Let's go ahead and start with bereavement, and we can catch Dr. Kazi up when he gets here," Carol rushed on.

"We only had one death this week. Grace," Tom, our team chaplain, began. Every week we talk about who has passed away and how the family and friends they left behind are coping. Most of the time, the friends include us.

"Grace was mine," I began. Blinking, I tried to control the tears welling up in my eyes. I knew I should talk about how her family was coping. Yet at that moment I could only think about

White Shoulders. I remembered smelling it in my bedroom, Twilla smelling it forty miles away, but most importantly, how Grace's breathing had eased when Penny rubbed it on her.

Tricia patted my hand, passed me a box of tissues, and continued for me. "I saw her, too, and I think the daughter, Penny, is going to be okay. The last time I talked to her she told me about her mother wanting her perfume on when she died, and she seemed to be comforted that Grace got what she wanted.

"How are you holding up, honey?" Tricia asked.

I took a deep breath, hoping the cold air would hold back a couple of renegade tears threatening to roll down my cheeks. "I'm fine. I never actually talked to her, which makes it a little easier. She was unresponsive when we admitted her. And I know she went very peacefully, which should be a comfort to the family."

"Hello, everybody!" Dr. Kazi called out, whisking into the room and rescuing me from a tear stained good-bye to Grace. He arrived in a hurry, just like he did everything else. His time was in demand at the hospital, his office, and at hospice. His gift was doling it out in the right doses.

"We had one death, Grace, who was Linda's patient up north," Carol said, efficiently bringing Dr. Kazi up to date. Dr. Kazi and Carol had an excellent working relationship since they seemed to be sprinting at the same pace to get things done.

"I remember her," he said, and I knew he did. Paying attention to all the details made him a great doctor.

"And we have one new admission, also up north, who will be Linda's: Michael Morton," Carol continued.

"I know him, they call him Mike. I saw him for Dr. Park at the hospital," Dr. Kazi interjected. "Nice man, very sad case. They found his cancer too late. You'll like his wife, too."

I smiled at Dr. Kazi and that thought. Our patients were almost never a problem, while family members could prove challenging. "Do I need any special equipment or supplies?"

"No, I don't think so. He gets around pretty good. Actually, he can still drive a car. Just call me for orders when you get there. It's been a few days since I've seen him and he could have had some changes."

"Let's get to current patients. Angela, you go first." Carol was still steering the ship forward, full speed ahead.

"Right, Anderson is first. Mrs. Anderson is quite a character. Eighty-nine years old, diagnosis of colon cancer. She tortures this poor woman who takes care of her. Tom, I really think she could use a chaplain visit."

"Has she asked for a chaplain visit?" Tom inquired.

"Well, yes and no." Angela explained. "I think she has issues to work through, lots of them actually. You or Tricia would be a tremendous help, but Mrs. Anderson thinks only poor people need social workers. She probably wouldn't give Tricia the time of day, if she even let her in the living room. I did tell her that hospice provides home visits by a chaplain, and like my other wealthy patients, she wants to get her money's worth out of us."

"Didn't she ask you for daily nurse visits at one time?" Carol interjected.

"Yeah, she did," Angela smiled. "I knew I couldn't tell her no. No one tells Mrs. Anderson no. I just told her I would love nothing more than to see her every day, and asked which time slot she would prefer, either six in the morning or eight in the evening. I know she's in bed by eight every night and she is not a morning person either. She never lets me visit before noon."

"What did she say to her choices?" Carol asked.

"No, of course. Then I pretended to be disappointed, to seal the deal."

Dr. Kazi was laughing to himself.

"My next two patients are Russian, so bear with me while I try to pronounce the names. Carol, why do I get all the Russians? I spend half my day sometimes on the phone with translation services!"

I turned my attention back to my paperwork mountains as Angela continued. Every patient has medication sheets that have to be reviewed and signed by the nurse weekly. These sheets include patient information, delivery address, medication allergies, current medications, refill dates, and discontinued or inactive drugs. My signature at the bottom of each patient's medication list indicates my agreement to the accuracy of all the information in that novella. Fortunately, or unfortunately, depending on the point of view, I can check this information as often as I want from my home computer. That gives me more time to make sure it's accurate before I sign off on it at the meeting. It's also time I'm ignoring Kevin, while not getting dinner cooked or dishes and laundry washed.

Once the three-inch stack of drug sheets had been signed, I pulled a small spiral notebook from my lab coat pocket. The pages have wrinkled into shapes that no longer resemble rectangles, with a spot on one page that I truly hope is ketchup. Next to the initials of each patient, I record things I couldn't possibly hold for a week in the overcrowded space between my ears. Besides numbers such as weights and vital signs, I make notes about patient falls. Just about any time someone touches the floor, or gets hurt in any way, an incident report is generated. Of course, that is not the only report needed during our weekly meeting. All patients on antibiotics have infection reports. All patients with less than perfect skin have wound reports.

These are hospice patients, people at the end of their lives. It would be far more efficient and environmentally friendly to file reports on those who didn't fall, have a wound, or take an antibiotic.

"Linda? Are you ready to report?"

I flipped open a blue binder, which I have organized

alphabetically. Each new patient has a case sheet, a single sheet of paper that has the address and phone numbers for the patient, their primary caregiver, other important friends and relatives if applicable, and their doctors. It also has the patient's birth date and diagnosis. Sometimes I jot down an anniversary or other important facts I may need to remember. Otherwise, the only thing I will write on the sheet eventually is the date of death. Then, I file it to the back of my binder in case I make a bereavement call or visit.

"First we have Faye out at Sunset Ranch," I began, turning to the first case sheet. Sunset Ranch is the assisted living facility where several of my patients reside. The guidelines for team meetings require us to read the full name, diagnosis, age, location, and basically all the other information everyone present can read on the agenda. Not being a fan of redundancy, I think of those guidelines as suggestions rather than rules. "She is so sweet. She never says a word anymore, and there is no evidence of pain. Tom, I know you visit her. Does she speak to you?"

"No, not a word. When I pray or read scriptures, some of the patients who don't usually speak actually pray along, but Faye doesn't. She does seem much happier now that she is living at the Ranch."

"She does," Tricia interjected. "That last assisted living facility was terrible. They left her in her room all day, half the time without even turning a light on. Now she sits in the dining area, or sometimes the activity area, and if she is in her room they have her chair turned so she can look out the window into the courtyard."

"I know. It makes me so happy for her. Anyway," I concluded, "she's fine. No change in her plan of care." I turned the page to my next patient's file. "Bonnie is next. She's the new patient in Sachse. I've called you about her, Dr. Kazi. She has increased weakness…"

"Yes, yes. I remember her. We started her on a low dose steroid this week."

"That's right, and I think we are about to need some long-acting morphine for pain. She's a tough one to judge. Bonnie tries to hide her pain."

Flipping to the next page in my binder, I saw Camellia's name and smiled to myself. "Let's see, then there's Camellia, also at the Ranch. She now has over half the staff in the facility convinced she is my mother. This week the hairdresser told me she just loves my mom."

"She is something else," Tricia said. "She sits at the dining table dousing everything she eats in Tabasco, then tells me she has stomach trouble."

"I know," I said with a grin. "Let's see… her weight is stable. She didn't fall this week. No change in her plan of care.

"Next is Eleanor, who is still planning her one hundredth

birthday party. Tricia, you are working on getting the recognition letter from the president for that, aren't you?"

"Right, I am. You have to start those things early to be sure you have them on time. I think she will make it to one hundred."

"So do I. She has been nearly one hundred in her mind since the day she turned ninety-nine. She did ask me if we could have her teeth whitened for the occasion. I told her that was a terrible idea. I'm not a dentist. Common sense, however, says that teeth that age probably won't survive any bleaching.

"Then there is Carlos. He is not at the Ranch, unfortunately. I think most of you know about this week's visit, since I called almost everyone and cried about it."

"It makes my skin crawl just thinking about it," Angela said with a shiver.

"Wait, I didn't hear this," Dr. Kazi said.

"You don't want to," Carol added with a frown.

"There are roaches all over his trailer. I don't even take the bag for my blood pressure cuff inside his house when I visit, because I am afraid roaches will crawl into it."

"I had to go see him when you were on vacation," Angela grimaced. "The floor crunched at times under my feet. I have never seen that many roaches!"

"I've called his son about it," Tricia said. "He knows how bad it is, but Carlos doesn't want to live with his son and won't allow an exterminator to come in. The son says Carlos has always lived this way."

"Do you still spray your shoes with bug spray before you go inside?" Dr. Kazi asked.

"Yes I do, and the bottoms of my pant legs. I do everything I can to prevent those nasty things from crawling up my legs. That just didn't help this time. I was almost finished with my visit when a huge black cockroach fell from the ceiling straight down the front of my shirt."

Moans filled the room, especially from the home health aides who had not suffered through my story already.

"Immediately, I grabbed the bottom of my shirt on each side to pull it over my head, my feet dancing all around his little kitchen. As soon as Carlos realized what I was about to do, he began clapping. He is always asking me to go dancing, and now he had me dancing in his kitchen and about to strip!"

One of the home health aides called out, "I would have done it, girl!"

"Well, I think his clapping and his laughing made me a little more aware that taking off my shirt was not the best plan. Luckily, I reached in and pulled that sucker out. I don't know what I would have done if I had missed it and it had run around under my clothes some more. Anyway, I grabbed it. When it hit the floor, I stomped it as hard as I could."

Dr. Kazi stared at me open-mouthed, looking appropriately appalled, while the home health aides sat shaking their heads in sympathy. It was over now. Talking about it still helped, especially with other people who knew it could have just as easily happened to them. Team meeting is supposed to be a Medicare requirement for planning patient care, and pulling a roach out of my shirt did not fit as a line item in the Medicare guidelines. What Medicare and hospice companies don't consider is that if the medical caregivers don't receive the support we need, there won't be anyone to provide care.

"She doesn't have to go back, does she, Carol?" Dr. Kazi asked.

"Actually, that was his last visit. He is the one we decided to take off for extended prognosis. When he is no longer wanting to go dancing and has some symptoms, we can revisit the idea of hospice."

"Then, someone else can be his nurse," I added.

"You know you'll take him back," Carol said flatly.

"She will," Angela agreed. I couldn't tell if her fingers were crossed beneath the table.

As the meeting concluded, I made a dash with the other nurses and the home health aides to the supply room. My goal remains the same: to have everything a patient could possibly want or need in my little yellow Beetle and never make a second trip to the office during the week.

"You have two bags of supplies from the list you e-mailed me," Whitney, our supply nurse, said as I turned the corner to the storage area. The room was utilitarian, gray metal shelving filled with everything from adult briefs and catheters to needles, syringes, and oxygen masks. "Don't forget the second bag. Are you going to need anything else?"

"No, that should do it," I said, eyeing the two large bags that had to be carried down to my car and loaded. If these were trash bags instead of clear plastic, they would be the thirty-gallon size used by landscapers and contractors. "I only have one admission today, in McKinney, and Dr. Kazi said I shouldn't need anything special."

"A patient close to home, aren't you lucky. See you next week," Whitney said as she briskly turned to fill the next bag.

It was only lunchtime and I was headed north again to McKinney. This evening I wouldn't have to battle Dallas traffic. A bit of my optimism was making a return.

CHAPTER 8

Driving to Mike's house was a pleasure. I was headed home. Kevin would be so pleased to have dinner at a reasonable time, and I could stop at a grocery store that I had actually been to before. Most people drive the same route to work day in and day out, but not me. I have had patients everywhere from my own neighborhood to fifty miles away. I prefer spending more time with patients than my windshield. It just doesn't always work that way. Of course, if hospice doesn't work out as a career for me, I would be a great pizza delivery driver. There isn't a house I can't find, eventually.

Mike's street was gracefully tree lined with lovely red brick houses. Each house was picture framed with shrubbery and flowers, and had a curved walkway leading to the mailbox. It was hard to believe that behind one of these perfect facades a man was dying of cancer. Cancer had nerve to intrude here. It never cares.

I pulled in the driveway and gathered my usual pile of paperwork, stethoscope, and blood pressure cuff. My new patient jitters were barely noticeable. The neighborhood was calm and peaceful, and Dr. Kazi had confirmed there would be no surprises inside.

Before I could ring the doorbell, the door swung open. "Hi, I'm Wendy, come on in." A slim woman with dark hair was cheerfully holding the door open for me. "Mike's watching television in the family room. He was out planting bushes in the landscape earlier. I made him come in and take a shower before you got here. Go on back and please excuse the mess. We just moved in last week."

"Thanks," I said as I lugged my stuff through the door. "You did just move." Instead of a manicured interior to match the exterior, the formal living room was piled with cardboard boxes. Some had been opened, with random contents strewn about, no doubt in a treasure hunt of sorts for a particular object. This move had been made in haste.

Walking down a short hall, I arrived in the family room. There, a fit looking man of about sixty was lounging on the sofa, watching the sports channel. His gray hair was cut short, yet he lacked the ravaged chemo look that Bonnie had. "Hi,

I'm Linda. I'll be your nurse," I said, moving the load to one arm so I could shake hands.

Mike looked at me intently. "I asked for a male nurse," he finally said.

"I'm sorry, I didn't know that. Usually we have more than our share of male nurses. There just isn't one on our team at the moment. We normally try to assign patients by geography. We send a nurse who lives close to you or who has other patients in your area. It improves our response time if you need us."

"That makes sense," said Wendy, who was now standing beside me in a show of solidarity. "Give her a chance, Mikey."

Mike was looking back at the television, unconvinced.

"We do have a male home health aide for when you need assistance with your bath…"

"I can shower just fine by myself," was his indignant reply. "It's not modesty. I just want someone I can talk to about sports. Now that I'm not working, there are no men around to talk to. Neither Wendy nor our daughter like football, or sports in general, and my son-in-law works most of the time…"

He had a touch of misplaced anger. In his shoes, who wouldn't? Breathing a sigh of relief, I said, "Well, if that's the only reason you want a male nurse, we'll get along just fine." Thinking of Camellia, who claims to be my mother instead of just a patient, and who is a former cook for the Dallas Cowboys, I added, "I even have a patient who will give me references."

"Do you follow the Cowboys?"

"Is the artificial turf green and the star at Texas Stadium blue?"

"What do you think of Tony Romo?"

"Undrafted, Eastern Illinois. I think they should give him a shot at quarterback. I'm tired of watching the washed-up, geriatric excuses for quarterbacks they've been playing. Is this a football team or an AARP meeting?" I shot back.

"So, are you going to take my blood pressure or what?"

"Yeah, I can do it now, but maybe not later. I'm hoping Jerry Jones comes to his senses and realizes we need a female coach in the NFL. I'm ready, and I've even picked out my offensive coordinator. She will whip those boys into shape," I said with a smile, thinking again of Camellia.

While checking his vital signs, I watched Mike for any signs of pain and didn't notice any. "I'm guessing you're not in a lot of pain if you were out working in the yard earlier?"

"Yeah, I don't really have any pain. I suppose I'm lucky there and maybe even lucky they found the cancer so late. I've been through a lot of testing, but no real treatment. I just wish I knew how much time I had. The last time I saw the oncologist he said I had a couple of weeks or maybe a couple of months. What do you think?"

Mike was looking me straight in the eye and I realized that, like Bonnie, he wanted a straight answer. Besides, he hadn't asked that question until Wendy stepped out of the room to answer the phone. "If that's what the oncologist told you, I would guess you had the weeks not the months."

"That's what I thought."

"You will have some control over it."

"What do you mean?" Mike asked, obviously interested.

"It just seems that people let go when they're ready. One day I had a patient who was actively dying at noon, breathing only about once a minute. I told the family she was going to pass away at any moment. They informed me she wouldn't die until after six that evening. While she had never had children, she was very close with a nephew. He was flying in to see her and would be at the house by six. I told them that people who only breathe once a minute don't live six hours."

"Did she?" Mike asked.

"Of course she did. She died at ten minutes past six, with her nephew at her side."

"So you're saying that if I need to see somebody or do something, I can hold on for that?"

"It certainly appears that way."

"There are a lot of things I want to do, like see my grandson grow up for one. Since that isn't going to happen, my primary concern was a business deal."

"Really? I've never had anyone talk much about business at the end. No one has ever said 'I wish I'd worked more.'"

"No," Mike said smiling. "It's not like that. I was working on a major deal when I got the news about the cancer. I needed everything to go through before I died so that Wendy would never have any money worries after my death. I just need to know she's taken care of, that's all."

"Has the deal gone through?"

"Just this afternoon," he grinned.

"Congratulations," I said, while I thought, *Good-bye.*

At seven the next morning my pager went off, with all the charm of a car alarm tucked into the pocket of my fuzzy white robe. With a mere half cup of coffee in my system, I jerked it from my pocket, grumbling. Kevin had brought in the newspaper, and my morning optimism had promised me a quick glance at the paper, along with a cup of coffee with my husband. After that, I had decided, I would start listening to voice mail, schedule visits, and in general, begin my day.

"What do they want now?" Kevin asked.

"Seriously, they can't call me until seven in the morning. Any calls that come in earlier go to the night shift. My guess is this came in at five or six and the night dispatcher just sat on it until they could call me," I said flatly. My anger faded into concern as I read the text message. "It says call Wendy. Wow, that was fast."

"Who is that?"

"It has to do with the new patient in McKinney, the one

considerate enough to live close to us so that I got home early last night."

"You still weren't home by five," he began.

"And I may never be, but we did have a decent dinner," I said bending down to give his upturned face a quick kiss. "Let me call her back, and then I'll let you know if I can finish my coffee."

Thoughts of a leisurely morning were vanquished with the call. Wendy hadn't said much on the phone, just asked rather desperately if I could come by as soon as possible. Almost before I could say yes, she thanked me and hung up. I had heard noises in the background, which I hoped were some television program. The tension in her voice told me that was wishful thinking.

The neighborhood looked typically suburban in the morning light. A few children were walking down the sidewalk, wearing school backpacks and smiles. Sunlight filtered through the trees, again belying the fact anything could be wrong behind this cheerful exterior. I pulled into the driveway and parked next to a car that hadn't been there yesterday. As I walked around the small SUV and headed up the sidewalk, I noticed a baby's car seat fastened in the back. It was early for a casual visit, even from family. My guess was Wendy had called both her daughter and me for help.

I tapped lightly at the door before turning the knob. If

the daughter had arrived, chances were the alarm would be turned off. I hadn't seen any dogs yesterday that might mistake me for breakfast, and those are details I make it a point to not overlook. "Wendy? Wendy, where are you?"

"Upstairs, Linda," came a strained response.

I took the stairs as quickly as possible. Halfway up I heard strange groans, mixed with nearly unintelligible words. The sounds I heard over the phone this morning had not been coming from a television.

"Dad, lay back down. Please, Dad."

Directed by sound, I found myself in the master bedroom. Unlike the formal living room, no boxes remained to be unpacked. Silk drapes hung from dark rods, gracefully puddling at the floor in front of multiple windows. The light-filled room was the perfect backdrop for the rich, dark wood furniture. The centerpiece was a king-size bed, with a tall, intricately detailed headboard. A red and gold finely striped dust ruffle adorned the bottom of the bed. It was matched by a thick comforter in the same tones and coordinating print, currently massed into a huge pile at the foot of the bed, where a wild-eyed Mike was kicking it hard with both feet.

Wendy and daughter were on either side of the bed, both perspiring with the effort required to hold him in place. Grabbing Mike's arm just below where Wendy had gripped him, I said, "It's all right, I have him. Wendy, you are going downstairs to get the comfort pack. It's that emergency box that was delivered by FedEx. You know where it is in the refrigerator so I'll hold him while you get it. Bring me that and two teaspoons."

Without question or comment she ran from the room. My impression of Wendy yesterday was thankfully accurate. She was capable and smart enough to know when to save questions for later.

"Mike, you are doing fine, and I promise, you'll feel much better in a moment. Hi, I'm Linda," I added by way of greeting to the twenty-something-year-old woman struggling across from me.

"Heather," she answered.

Mike twisted side to side at the sound of Heather's voice, a guttural sound emanating deep from within. Men undergoing dungeon tortures in the Dark Ages have probably sounded better.

"You're doing a great job, Heather. We will have your dad calmed down in no time. I promise."

Tears began to glisten in her eyes. She had done what she thought was needed, never faltering until help had arrived. Heather was thin like her mother and fortunately had an athletic build. Her hair was pulled back in a ponytail, and it appeared she had been sleeping in the gray yoga pants and pink t-shirt she was wearing.

"Here it is," Wendy said breathlessly, waving a white box successfully in the air, two spoons in her other hand.

"Here is his arm back. Mike, try to not fight Heather and Wendy for a minute if you can," I said, making sure Wendy again had a grip before I stepped away.

Pulling my bandage scissors from my lab coat pocket, I cut the outer seal on the comfort pack box. Inside the box were three smaller boxes, each holding a bottle of a different emergency liquid medication. Besides the liquids, there were plastic bags of assorted pills. Finding the right package of pills, I cut open the plastic and popped one pill from a blister pack into a spoon. Using the other spoon, I crushed the pill to a fine powder. Opening the bottle of liquid morphine, I measured the dose with the dropper and put it in the spoon with the crushed pill.

"No!" Mike screamed nonsensically, and then reverted back to his groaning.

"It started about eleven last night," Wendy said, still breathless from the jaunt down and back up the stairs. Yesterday's mascara was smudged beneath her eyes. "He tried to jump out the window. He didn't just try once either. He kept trying, and talking out of his head. At first he made some sense, his words, I mean. Now we don't understand anything he is trying to say."

"Mom called me and I came right over," Heather explained.

"I waited until five to call her. By then I had to have help. We moved to McKinney as quickly as we could when Mike was diagnosed. He thought it was important for us to have Heather nearby in case we needed her. I just hate to disturb her sleep after she has chased after a toddler all day."

"Mom, you should have called me at eleven when it first started," Heather interrupted.

"What is wrong with him, Linda? He was out in the yard planting shrubs yesterday and now he's berserk. The doctor said the cancer hasn't metastasized to his brain."

"He's not berserk, actually. He has what we call terminal agitation," I said as I approached the bed, holding the spoon tightly in case he lunged at me. "Mike, it's Linda again, your football-loving nurse. Open your mouth for me."

I held up the spoon for Wendy and Heather to see, nodding in the direction of Mike. "Ideally, we will get the contents of this spoon under his tongue. I will settle for anywhere in his mouth, preferably not spat back in my face."

As if on cue, Mike wailed again, allowing me the perfect access to dump the contents of the spoon in his mouth.

"What was that?" Wendy and Heather chimed in unison.

"Morphine, mixed with lorazepam. Lorazepam is in the same family as Xanax and Valium, and is a fast-acting medication. It comes in liquid form, but the comfort pack only has it in pill form. I crushed it between the spoons so he can't choke on it or spit it out as easily. Adding the liquid morphine to it makes the powder dissolve somewhat. I call it a Jell-O shooter."

Heather shook her head. "I don't follow you."

"Once that combination enters his body, Mike will have the consistency of gelatin, or Jell-O. Don't worry. It won't hurt him. He will, however, calm down and go to sleep."

"Other hospice patients act this way?" Wendy asked as she tried to digest everything she had just heard.

"Yes, except not exactly like this," I answered. "When people are dying, they become agitated. It is usually a long process. Most patients are bedbound by then," I said as images of Bonnie popped into my head. "There are some dramatic differences with Mike. He didn't become weak from the treatments since he never had treatment. He didn't follow the pattern of becoming bedbound and then developing terminal agitation. He went straight into it, so instead of just being restless, possibly calling out or waving his hands in the air..."

"He tried to jump out the window," Wendy finished for me.

"Exactly."

"Other people really have done this?" Heather asked, obviously trying to reconcile the actions of her father with known possibilities.

"Yes. I knew of a man who behaved not unlike Mike is

behaving for three straight days."

"Couldn't you control it?" Wendy asked.

"No, no, it wasn't that. It was the husband of a friend of mine, another hospice nurse actually. He was only in his late forties and like Mike they had discovered his cancer too late for treatment. He wandered their house three days and three nights, behaving much the same as Mike."

"I don't know how she managed for three days," Wendy said, closing her eyes and rubbing her forehead.

"I have no idea how she managed either. It was actually her husband's death that prompted her to become a hospice nurse. I only wish he had been my patient. No one, neither she nor her husband, should have suffered through that."

Mike had calmed down enough that Wendy and Heather had both begun to relax with him.

"Terminal agitation you called it? Terminal?" Heather said sadly.

"That's right. I'm sorry."

"How long does he have? Will he get like this again? I don't know if I can stand it if he makes another attempt to jump out the window. He had no idea what he was doing." Tears fell slowly as Wendy spoke. The storm had subsided for a moment and the emotions held in check since last night came forth.

I grabbed her into a bear hug as tears changed to sobs. "Last night is over. I promise. You will have to put up with me for a while longer. I am going to get orders for a nurse to stay with Mike around the clock. We will need a hospital bed and a few other pieces of equipment and medication orders. Someone will stay with you until the end. And with the right medication, you won't have a repeat of last night. Heather, before you leave, I might need you to make a trip to the pharmacy for me to get some more medication for your dad."

Mike's decline progressed as quickly as it had begun. I kept my promise of supplying equipment, medications, and Continuous Care. Heather made arrangements for a friend to take care of her two-year-old so she could stay with Wendy. None of this mattered to Mike. His last business deal was tied up neatly with a bow, a gift of financial protection for Wendy. He passed away peacefully that very night.

Two weeks later I was still trying to find the time to make a bereavement visit to Wendy. She was new in town and practically my neighbor. Despite being tired and anxious to get home, I finally called her and arranged to stop by.

Hoisting myself out of the car, I again admired the neighborhood. Suburban America dressed at its best. The brick facades glowed in the warmth of the late afternoon sun. The homes resembled each other like children in a family, yet like children, each one had unique characteristics. Large, welcoming front windows were the most distinguishing feature of Wendy's home. Beneath the windows, small shrubs were carefully arranged in the landscape, mounds of fresh mulch at their feet. The plastic tags from the nursery remained fastened to each plant, identifying the type of plant and the care instructions. My attention was drawn to those tags as they rustled in the light afternoon breeze, while my thoughts drifted to the man who had planted them.

"I was hoping you would call," Wendy said, holding the door open for me. She was dressed in jeans and an oversized Dallas Cowboys sweatshirt. Her shoulder length dark hair was pulled back in a ponytail, emphasizing how much she and Heather looked alike. Dark circles or reddened puffiness were notably absent from her eyes. The anguished appearance I might have expected in a new widow was missing.

"This room doesn't look any better than the last time you were here," she said, smiling as we sat on the couch. Cardboard moving boxes remained stacked against a wall with a couple of open ones on the floor.

"You've had a busy month, and that's an understatement. How have you been?" I asked as I tried to reconcile Wendy's serene demeanor with the chaotic appearance of the room.

"I'm good, actually. While I miss Mike terribly, it's been nice having Heather and her family close by."

"Do you see them often? I remember that was Mike's purpose in wanting to buy this house."

"Yes, and that brings me to something I want to tell you.

That's why I was really hoping you would come by soon."

Guilt pinched me. I wished I had called sooner. Twenty-four is such a stingy number of hours to have in the day.

"So last week, about a week after Mike died, Heather was here with little Carson, our grandson. We've been trying to potty train him, but you know how boys are. He screams every time we sit him on the potty chair."

"Boys do seem resistant to potty training," I added, wondering where this story was headed.

"Heather and I were standing in the bathroom with Carson sitting on the potty, screaming and crying. His little face turned red with tears just streaming down those chubby cheeks of his. You would think we were torturing him. Suddenly he stopped crying and started giggling. Heather and I hadn't moved a muscle, yet he was squirming and laughing so hard you would have thought one of us was tickling him. Heather asked him, 'Carson, what are you laughing at?' Between giggles he caught his breath, and looking just past us said, 'Grandpa Mikey is making funny faces.'"

I looked at Wendy. Words failed me. Finally under my breath, I managed to say, "Wow!"

"I know," she said. "It's pretty amazing. I'd love to see Mike myself, but knowing Carson saw him is just about as good."

Losing Mike had not taken me by surprise. That didn't make it any easier to lose a patient. It did make me feel better to know that Wendy had Heather and her family nearby. Mike's parting gift to Wendy had been more than financial security. He had given her emotional security by moving her near their daughter.

Then there was little Carson.

He saw Mike. There was just no other explanation. A two-year-old can't make up something like that. He couldn't go from tears to laughter unless something or someone prompted him to do so. He also couldn't elaborate on precisely what he saw and heard. Manuel's great-grandson had seen him after his death. Now Mike's grandson had seen him. I had told Bonnie that God wasn't from a Renaissance painting and that heaven didn't have harps and halos. Maybe I need to recruit children to teach what heaven is really like.

CHAPTER 9

August 1970

Today I drove for the very first time. I'm ten years old and I have driven a car. At least, I mostly drove a car. I steered by myself, nice and straight. I didn't go off the road at all. I kept one eye on the road and one eye on the pedals in case I needed to hit the brake. Daddy woke up before I had to hit the brake.

We are Ford people, and have both a 1965 Mustang and a 1968 Torino. That makes up a lot for living in a house with only one real bedroom and no bricks. Mama always picks out the car. I think she does a good job. When Daddy and I are out driving, I feel rich like the kids at school. Today, Daddy and I drove the Torino. It's a color called diamond blue. I know the exact name of the color because Mama says it so often.

Everyone who sees the Torino says it's a pretty car, a pretty white car, which upsets Mama. She would never buy a plain white car, or a plain white anything. Maybe Ford should have named it barely blue.

Daddy and I go for long drives in the country, something we've done together since I was little. During the school year we go after school, but in the summer we can go anytime we feel like it since Daddy doesn't tend bar until the evening. My favorite part of the drive is a long stretch of road where the trees are as tall as the sky and at the top their branches reach over the road and touch in the middle. It's like riding through a dark, leafy tunnel. It's even as dark as a tunnel because the trees are so thick, and the mossy smell of earth and leaves drifts in through the open car windows. When a breeze blows, bits of sunlight break through and dance across the hood of the car. The whole time we are in this wooded tunnel, I think of all the fairytales I've ever heard with an enchanted forest in them. I am the princess, of course, even if my carriage has horsepower without real horses.

For a while now, there have been times when Daddy closes his eyes while he's driving. I've been learning to watch the road more often than the tree branches and sunlight. Usually I just say, "Daddy wake up!" Then he opens his eyes right away, looks a little startled, and grabs the wheel tighter. His knuckles look white for a minute and then he relaxes.

"Are you okay?" he always asks, glancing at me.

"I'm fine. You just had your eyes closed for a second," I tell him.

When he closed his eyes today, they didn't open when I called his name. His head was hanging a little bit forward, not one dark hair out of place. He was sleeping peacefully behind the wheel of the car. I held my breath and thought about what I should do. I didn't want to startle him. Sometimes if my grandmother, Nina, wakes me up suddenly it startles me a bit. Then I jump, because for a split second, I don't know what's going on. I really didn't want to make Daddy jump. He might jerk the steering wheel and slam us right into a tree or another car.

All these thoughts raced through my head in the blink of an eye that felt like an hour. I had to wake him up. I couldn't risk scaring him. He was our driver. He had to drive. Gently, I touched his shoulder. Nothing happened. Feeling braver now that I hadn't sent us hurtling into oncoming traffic, I shook him harder. Nothing. I scooted over and grabbed the wheel. We weren't going too fast; we never do, because Daddy says the drive lasts longer if you take it slow. It wasn't hard. I held the wheel just like I had always seen Mama and Daddy do. Luckily, his foot had slipped off the gas pedal. I put my left leg over Daddy's right leg in case I needed to hit the brake.

The road was only one lane in each direction so I knew I

needed to stay on our side of the yellow stripe. There was one stupid tree after another along the side of the road as I steered through the tunnel. Those trees don't look as pretty when you realize you could hit one of them! I didn't want to do that anymore than I wanted to cross the stripe and hit another car. I held it steady, but I was worried when he didn't wake up. We were still rolling forward, in our own lane, when his eyelids blinked. As soon as he realized where I was sitting and that I was holding the wheel, his eyes flew wide open again.

"I've got it," he said, once again taking the steering wheel.

He looked more than a little scared. I was worried about Daddy, but hadn't had time to be really upset until he seemed to be. "Was I out long?" he asked.

I had let go of the wheel and pulled my left leg away. I scooted more to the middle of the big bench seat but not too far. Just in case. "No, well, it seemed long. I called your name and touched your arm. When you didn't wake up I thought I should steer. Did you see I had my foot ready to hit the brake?"

"You were great, sweetheart. I'm really proud of you. I'm just sorry you had to do that." He didn't look so good. In spite of the breeze from the open window, beads of sweat dotted his forehead. His face was pale white with a hint of blue, just like the Torino.

Daddy looked so scared and kind of sick in the car today. It was time to find out what was going on before coming home from school again to the sound of moans from behind the French doors, or finding out that he'd been taken off to the hospital. They still won't let me visit him there because you have to be twelve. Everyone guesses my age at about eight now so I could never pass for twelve.

For once I was glad we live in the little house that my grandfather built. I think of it as a God-bless-you house. It's so small that no matter where you are when you sneeze everyone under the roof will respond with either *"Gesundheit"* or "God bless you." Right now, I don't care that it only has four rooms and no bricks. I just want to know if Daddy is having another stroke or something.

The best time to find out anything is in the middle of the night when I am supposed to be asleep. Mama gets up at quarter past five every weekday morning. I have heard her mention a few times that it is the only time of day she feels she has the house to herself. She makes her breakfast and packs her lunch, and then heads to the factory for first shift. Daddy, on the other hand, comes home around two o'clock in the morning. He and Mama can't both work in the morning. There isn't much need for a bartender that early in the day. Their time together is in the small hours when Daddy comes home. While Nina and I sleep, Mama always gets up for a bit with Daddy. I never hear her get up so I don't know if she sets her alarm or if Daddy wakes her up, or if she just somehow knows it's their time.

A lot has changed in the three years since Daddy had his stroke. I've grown up, of course, even if no one ever guesses that I'm ten years old. With two digits in my age, I'm practically a teenager. Now that my sister has graduated college and moved out of the house, I'm in her old room. Nina and I have the real bedroom with twin beds, right next to the kitchen. Mama bought us beautiful new sheets with bright psychedelic designs. My sister only wanted plain white sheets, plain just like her.

It is great having a real bedroom and my very own bed. I can stretch out and move around all I want without kicking Nina. Best of all, I can hear Mama and Daddy talk in the kitchen when he gets home from work.

That is the perfect time to get the information I need. Tonight I waited for them. I could smell the leftovers as Mama reheated our dinner for Daddy. Sometimes we have breaded pork chops and egg noodles. That's when Nina has cooked. She only makes German style food like her mother taught her. My favorites when Mama cooks are either meatloaf or chicken and dumplings. Mama says her dumplings are always too thick, not as good as Aunt Ruth's. I love them the way Mama makes them. And I love anything with her brown gravy on it. If there is extra gravy, I eat it over a slice of white bread.

The smell of dinner drifts through the house again at two a.m. when Daddy gets home. I can sometimes hear the clank of a pot lid, but they are usually quiet like mice and hard to hear.

Their voices are often just whispers. I can tell when it's Mama speaking or Daddy, but can't always make out the words. I like to wake up then because hearing them together, even just the hum of their whispered words muffled by the oak door between the kitchen and bedroom, is the best and safest sound in the world.

Tonight wasn't so quiet. Mama sounded upset. I could hear everything without any effort at all. Nina was snoring in her bed, which I hoped would somehow disguise my wakefulness. "Maybe you shouldn't take her out anymore," Mama was saying.

"She did great. You should have seen her holding the steering wheel. Don't worry, it won't happen again."

"She's ten years old! Honey, she could have been killed. You both could have been killed."

"I know. I promise nothing's going to happen to her. I won't ever let anything happen to Linda."

"You mean you're going to stop driving, except to work?"

"No," Daddy answered. "I mean I'm going to quit falling asleep when I drive. She loves to go out. I'll be careful with her."

I still wanted to go for our drives, even though today really had scared me. That is our special time together. Daddy will just have to be careful and stay awake like he told Mama. Even though my eyelids were growing heavy I could still hear them talking. Now the topic was heart blockages and blood thinners. Mama said blood thinners cause the bruising. I wondered why if he barely bumped his arm, there would be a huge bruise. One day, his blood won't be thin enough to get through some kind of blockages and he will die. That can't be right. I must have misunderstood. Maybe I was dreaming.

In the morning, with the light peeking in through the gap between the roller shade and the window frame, nothing seemed so bad. I looked over at Nina's empty bed with the spread already pulled up for the day and thought about what I heard last night. Daddy's heart is sick. That's what all the talk of heart blockages and blood thinners was about. When he got sick three years ago, everyone said he hadn't been taking care of himself. Now he has. I know he's even gained some weight because he got some new clothes. I went with Mama to Sears to get the shirts, but he had the suit made at the tailor. The more I thought about it, the easier it became to sweep all the talk of sickness under a rug. I had probably just dreamed the part about heart blockages and Daddy dying.

I'd rather think about the new suit. Daddy will look so handsome in it. I'm just not sure why Daddy had to get a new suit. He and Mama never go to church. Actually, they did go once. It was the Easter Sunday I made my First Holy Communion. Together we all piled into the wooden pew in the very front row of the church. Sunlight streamed in through the window and I thought the pastel painted cinder block building was touched by heaven. Sitting between Daddy in his suit and tie and Mama in her bright Easter dress and high heels was better than car rides with Daddy. The priest even mentioned us and how great it was that I had picked the day of the resurrection to make my communion.

Today though, Daddy's new suit will just hang in the closet. Daddy will wear trousers and a white t-shirt, socks and slippers. Mama will wear her denim pedal pushers and a sleeveless blouse. I will wear my brown plaid Sunday dress, handed down to me from my cousin, and Nina will wear her standard issue grandmother clothes, one of several unremarkable dark dresses that hang well below her knees, revealing a glimpse of support hose and sensible shoes.

Before Nina had time to come wake me, I crawled out of bed. Sunday is my favorite day and I didn't want to waste any of it. It is the only day of the week we are all together most of the day like a real television family. I slipped the cool, well-worn cotton dress over my head and began combing my hair for church. I had to be ready on time since Nina and I ride there with Mrs. Foster our neighbor across the street.

After Mass was over, we cruised back home in Mrs. Foster's Impala. The vinyl seats made the back of my dress sticky with sweat. Without waiting for Nina, I ran up the steps to the front porch, past the hydrangea bushes and white planters spilling red geraniums, anxious for the good part of Sunday to begin. The temperature on the porch already felt a million degrees cooler than Mrs. Foster's car. As the door swung open, the chilled air-conditioned air hit me, carrying with it the smell of fresh coffee mingled with Sunday lunch. "Hi Daddy! Is there gravy, Mama?" I asked, running the few steps from the living room, past Daddy watching television on their bed, into the kitchen.

"There will be if you let me finish up," Mama said. "You have to get Daddy to the table if you want to eat."

Nina joined Mama in the kitchen. Her sensible church shoes had been discarded in favor of even more sensible white sneakers. With Nina tying her apron in place around her ample waist, I was free from any type of work, which is just the way I like it.

"Daddy, come on," I pleaded. "Dinner is ready and we can't eat until you come to the table."

"Let me watch the rest of this inning, then I'll think about it," he said, giving me a playful grin.

I bounced up beside him on the bed and he wrapped an arm around me. "Is it Cincinnati?" They're our team. Kentucky doesn't have sports teams so sometimes we go to Cincinnati and watch the Reds play a game.

"Look, the bases are loaded."

I glanced at the color television and then to the dresser

mirror. Our faces were reflected back from the mirror with the light from the television casting a changing glow on us. My stomach growled, but sitting snuggled up with Daddy is almost as good as brown gravy. Half watching the game and half watching the mirror, I resumed my pleading.

"He struck out so I suppose we can eat," Daddy said, giving me a squeeze.

Bouncing back off the bed I walked the few steps into the kitchen with Daddy's hand in mine, just for insurance. I didn't want him to stop halfway there and start fine-tuning the color on the set or begin watching another inning.

Quickly we took our places around the red Formica and chrome kitchen table. The kitchen was crowded when no one was in it and by the time we pulled chairs out to sit down it was fairly bursting. One wall holds the sink, with running water that arrived the same year I did. On the next wall is the big gas stove, and in the corner sits our one truly modern appliance, a refrigerator with a pullout freezer drawer. It is a direct result of Mama working in the factory where such marvels are made. In between these kitchen staples, miscellaneous cabinets are crammed in, along with a collection of doors. Behind Daddy's chair are the back door and the door to the bathroom, also added on the year running water and I arrived. Then, there is a door to the attic, one to the basement, and of course, one to the real bedroom, and one to the repurposed dining room.

My plate was as crowded as the room. Mama always says my eyes are bigger than my stomach. Daddy had a full plate, too. There can't be anything to worry about. When I'm sick, I don't want to eat.

"I told Ruth I'd stop by today or tomorrow," Mama was saying.

"Why don't you go tomorrow evening when I'm at work?" Daddy replied.

No mention of sickness. Everything was okay. I spooned some peas into my mouth before Mama could tell me I couldn't possibly live on gravy alone, and tried to find a way to join the conversation.

"I have to write Miss Lottie another letter today after we eat," I proclaimed with an air of self-importance. Having a pen pal sounds so grown-up and makes me feel special. Lottie Carmichael lives in a nursing home. My whole class was assigned an old person to write letters to, and I got Miss Lottie. Everyone laughed about her old-fashioned name but I don't care. I write to her almost every day. I tell her about Mama and Daddy and Nina, and about our boxer dog Buddy. There is always something to tell her.

"Tell Miss Lottie I said hello," Daddy said as he pushed his chair away from the table. "Dinner was great. Now I'm going to take a little nap."

Mama reached for her cigarettes and lighter. "Linda, you

go outside and play so you don't wake Daddy up. You can write your letter in a bit. Nina and I will clean up these dishes as soon as I finish this cigarette and have some coffee."

Playing outside in August was a hot task, but with Buddy's companionship I could ignore the heat, at least for a while. Finally, deciding Buddy and I were both hot and thirsty, we went back inside to the kitchen. "Be quiet," Mama cautioned again.

"I'm just going to get a glass of milk and write my letter to Miss Lottie."

Mama and Nina were still drinking coffee and contemplating the need for dishwashing as I worked on my letter. Page after page of notebook paper I filled, leaving no small detail out about my day. I call her my pen pal, even if Miss Lottie is too old to write me back. I did get to meet her on a field trip to the old folks home. All the old people made a big deal out of me because apparently Miss Lottie is the only one who gets a letter almost every day. Some of the other kids only wrote once. That's okay, because Miss Lottie shares my letters with everyone. They all felt that they knew me, and Nina, and Mama and Daddy, and Buddy the boxer. Finally, another long installment of life at 2724 Birchwood Avenue was completed to my satisfaction.

"Mama, I need a stamp for my letter," I announced as I licked the envelope shut.

"They're in the bedroom. Go ask Daddy for a stamp. He's

probably ready to get up from his nap by now. He's been asleep a long time."

Skipping away from the table, white envelope in hand, I went in search for yet another six-cent stamp. Mama and Daddy never seem to mind that I am spending so much money on Miss Lottie. "Daddy, I need a stamp for my pen pal letter," I called out as I turned the doorknob.

Walking across the glossy hardwood floors, the rubber soles of my tennis shoes didn't make a sound, but a floorboard creaked as I stepped toward the bed. Daddy was in his usual spot on his side of the bed, stretched out just where he had been when I came home from church. His eyes were closed. The ballgame wasn't on now. The color television sat silent and dark.

My tennis shoes suddenly stuck as though they were glued to the floorboards. There was a streak of white running through Daddy's dark hair that I had never seen before. It started at his forehead and cut a line through his hair like a part. Where did it come from? How did it get there? Finally, tearing my eyes away from the white streak in his hair, I looked down at his t-shirt. I watched his chest for a long time. His white t-shirt was still. It should be moving up and down with each breath, but it wasn't.

With effort, I lifted first one glued foot, then the other, and silently tiptoed toward Daddy. I still couldn't see the rise and fall of his chest. Finally, when I was close enough to touch him, I let my fingers slide across the back of his hand. It wasn't like the other day in the car when his warm hands took the wheel from me. Instead, his hand was cool against my fingers. And I knew he wasn't going to be startled or jump, even if I shook him. I just knew.

With his eyes closed and a peaceful expression on his face, he looked like he always did when he was sleeping. I tried to force my eyes away from the white streak in his hair. As long as I didn't look at that, or touch his hand, it was easy to believe he was sleeping. Just sleeping.

My heart was beating so hard it was ready to burst from my chest. I put one foot behind the other like a tightrope walker and stepped back slowly and carefully. The toe of my tennis shoe nearly scraped the heel of the shoe in front of it with each tiny backward step. I had come in through the door to the kitchen, but I couldn't go back that way. Mama and Nina were still in the kitchen. My tightrope led me instead to the French doors and the living room. Finally, I made it out the front door.

Then I ran.

Taking the concrete steps two at a time, I was off the porch and in the yard in a flash. My bicycle with the banana seat and wicker basket on the handlebars was sprawled in the yard where I had abandoned it last. I jumped on and pedaled as fast as I could down the gravel drive and into the street. Our street is called the hill. Today it might be flatland for how fast I climbed it, repeating to myself, "Daddy can't be dead."

My heart pounded even harder and I couldn't catch my breath. I kept riding. The pedals went around and around with my thoughts. *Daddy can't be dead. Daddy loves me. He will give me away at my wedding. Daddy will give me away at my wedding. He will. That's what fathers do.*

Tears streaked my face and I brushed them away with my arm. My side hurt from pedaling so fast. *Daddy will be okay. Daddy has to be okay. He is going to give me away at my wedding. He has to.*

I found myself at school. The cinder block building was attached to the matching church building. Mass was over for the day and the buildings sat baking in the summer sun surrounded by an empty blacktop parking lot. The vacant swing set and sliding board stood to one side of the school building, motionless in the hot still air. How could everything look so normal?

Putting one foot down, I balanced the bike, lowered my head, and gasped for air. The last of my tears dried in streaks on my face. After a few more deep breaths I finally took one that didn't hurt. Turning the handlebars, I pointed myself in the direction of home. The wheels rolled along at an unhurried pace now. My feet were weighted with lead as I pushed first one pedal around then the other. My thoughts matched my bike-riding pace with their own slow revolution. *Daddies take their daughters to baseball games. Daddies take their daughters for long drives in the country. Daddies walk their daughters down the aisle on their wedding days.*

The lies I told myself just couldn't hold together. They were thin and transparent, like a white cloud blown apart by a hot summer breeze.

My daddy was dead. It was time to go home.

CHAPTER 10

Tired was creeping up on me. I was tired of thinking in circles and tired of working. The weight of the world, or more likely my arthritis, was making my back and shoulders ache. I had just visited Bonnie again, and climbing back into the Volkswagen, I pulled out my small spiral notebook to jot down my odometer reading. Eighty miles. After arriving at my first patient's home this morning, which had been more than twenty miles from my house, I had driven another eighty miles to see three more people. Traffic could also be contributing to the ache in my shoulders that was now making its way up my neck to the back of my head. Physically I was tired, but also emotionally. I had covered many of those miles thinking about Wendy and Mike. Bonnie had only been my fourth patient visit of the day. Even if I wanted nothing more than to go home, company policy was five visits a day with no slack allowed for headaches or heartaches.

Unable to mask the weariness and present the attentive and professional appearance my patients deserved, I headed north. I needed welcoming arms and a comfortable chair. I needed to talk about sports and what was for dinner. I needed a break to talk about living instead of dying.

I went to see Camellia.

Camellia and a few of my other patients live in the sprawling facility called Sunset Ranch. It's a luxury to have several patients who share not only a zip code but also the same roof. The fact that it is near my house is the icing on the cake. More important than the proximity to my house, however, is the care provided by the staff there. If I had elderly parents who needed more care than I could provide, the Ranch is exactly the kind of home I would choose for them. Visitors can drop in on Mom or Grandpa, unannounced, and stay for dinner. The food will be both recognizable and enjoyable. There are no strange smells wafting down the halls, and the staff is more likely to be found in a resident's room than sitting behind a desk.

I pulled into the parking lot and parked as far away from the door as possible. Visitors are frequently friends or siblings of the residents, many of them older than the residents themselves. Their driving and parking skills are too often of the bumper car style for my liking. A distant space remains my best defense. Besides, walking across the parking lot would likely be the only exercise I would get today. My joints still ached, even as the tension in my neck began to ease. A cold wind tossed my hair in a swirl around my face, while cutting through the lightweight cotton of my lab coat. Motivated by the cold, I walked a little faster, trying to ignore those annoying joints.

Besides concern for my car, I had very little to worry about at the Ranch. My hospice patients were not only well cared for by the staff, they were loved. The staff is almost exclusively comprised of nurse's aides, sans nurses. Assisted living facilities are not required to have a plethora of licensed staff, nor do they need it. Residents need the kind of care provided in past generations by extended family. They don't need state of the art medical care. They need a home. The Ranch aides assist with everything from bathing to getting them to the dining room for meals, while treating the residents like they were cherished grandparents. New staff members who don't accept the residents as surrogate grandparents are quickly weeded out.

I pulled one of the big wooden double doors open, and blew inside along with a gust of wind. It took a minute for my eyes to adjust to the dimness indoors after being in the bright sunlight. The smell of food cooking greeted me, reminding me to glance at the chalkboard menu before I headed back to Camellia's room. It really wasn't dinnertime yet, but octogenarians seem to have a different schedule than the rest of us, especially for mealtime and bedtime.

"It's about time you got here."

"Hi, Lloyd. How's it going today?" An older gentleman, wearing a red and black checked Western shirt, creased dark jeans and a big smile had rolled quietly up to me in his electric wheelchair just as the door slammed shut behind me. He's the Ranch equivalent of a cheerful Walmart greeter.

"Not too bad. It's been pretty quiet today. The church people were here this morning, singing and such. How cold is it out there?"

Lloyd needs the kind of assistance the Ranch provides. Besides the wheelchair, a large oxygen tank on the back of his chair provides a clue to his health issues. His mind, however, seems to be aging much more slowly than his body. He gets bored and is always eager to see a face from the outside.

"That sunshine is a bit deceiving. It wouldn't be too bad if someone would turn the wind off, or if it would at least quit blowing at gale force out of the north," I said as I pulled a pen from my pocket and signed the logbook for visiting medical staff. A quick glance through the signatures told me none of my coworkers were in the building this afternoon. "I think it was fifty-eight degrees according to the temperature gauge in my car, but the wind chill feels more like thirty-eight."

"That's a little cool for me. I think I'll stay inside," Lloyd responded, his last words interrupted by a harsh cacophony emitted from the foyer.

"Shut up, you stupid birds! I can barely hear myself think," Lloyd grumbled, rolling away from me. He headed over to a row of oversized birdcages occupied by exotic birds. Their incessant shrieking and squawking provide the residents with something to enjoy complaining about.

There are days I spend more of my waking hours at the Ranch than even my own home. If I had to make a fifth visit today, at least it was in comfortably familiar surroundings. Artificial flowers and plants bloom from vases and urns around the birdcages, providing the birds an equally artificial habitat. The greenery is not contained to the entryway. It has spread, weed-like, popping up at random from baskets and other containers throughout the building. It is accented by a rainbow of mismatched artwork flowing at eye level down each hall. There are enough gilt-framed pictures in the Ranch to fill a small museum, especially if the statues peeking out here and there from behind the potted plants were included in the collection. Nothing quite matches and there is definitely too much of everything.

This decorating chaos turns into a full assault on the senses at Christmas. Then layers of red, green, gold, and glitz are added to everything. The statues each find themselves standing next to a different, and possibly musical, Santa. Sometimes Santa is accompanied by a reindeer or two or even a singing snowman. The maintenance men devote weeks right up to Christmas Eve suspending garlands from every pillar and post, decorating multiple Christmas trees, and adding a thick layer of bling over all of it. Of course, when it all lights up, inside and outside, the Ranch glows. So do the residents.

Most of the year, or at least January through the middle of October, the home maintains some level of decorum. My teammate Angela visits my Ranch patients occasionally and claims it feels like a funeral parlor. I prefer to see the charm of a rambling Grandma's house. With her birds for company, it could belong to a little old lady who never gets rid of anything. She manages to find a space for any odd trinket a grandchild gives her, no matter how gaudy. In medical terms, it would be Grandma's house on steroids.

Making my way past potted ferns and screaming birds I passed the beauty shop on my way to Camellia's room. The beauty shop was dark behind the large picture window. Earlier today, it would have been a hive of activity. Countless ladies would have come in with thinning locks and left with true Texas oil baron hair. Like the salon, the activity room and halls were deserted as residents readied themselves for dinner. Some were adding a bit more spray lacquer to their hair, while others were watching television or taking a fortifying pre-dinner nap.

Camellia, I knew from experience, would be glued to the TV. She was legally blind, but her favorite pastime was watching sports on television. Her loyalties changed with the seasons. Football, defined by her as the Dallas Cowboys, was her favorite sport. The Texas Rangers and baseball managed a close second. She liked basketball and hockey, known here as the Mavericks and the Stars, but said they were too fast paced for her to follow. Her vision just couldn't keep up with basketballs and hockey pucks sailing across her big screen television.

Camellia's high spirits, unlike her vision, had not dimmed with age. If she loved you, she told you. If she thought you were an idiot, she wouldn't dip the message in sugar coating and candy sprinkles before she delivered it. She had African-American friends when white America still called them colored people, or worse. Camellia was a staunch, lifetime Democrat in Republican Texas. A young Elvis Presley had once kissed a young Camellia. Having a strong dislike for people who were "full of themselves," as she called it, she only mentioned that kiss one time while talking about a trip to Las Vegas.

In spite of her spirited approach to life, she was for all intents and purposes at the end of it. Now she navigated a rolling walker through the halls of the assisted living facility even if she couldn't see where she was going and her knees frequently gave out. She had more than one terminal illness on her chart and several more chronic health conditions. None of that interested her too much.

When we met she was angry that her son had put her on hospice, not because she was afraid of dying, but because her home health nurse had become a good friend. She didn't want to switch from home health to hospice for fear that I would turn out to be a jackass. The fact that I am a rabid Dallas Cowboys fan in winning seasons and in losing ones convinced her immediately of both my intelligence and our compatibility. It wasn't long before she told me I was her daughter. Camellia said she had adopted me because everyone needs a mother.

I could hear the sports report blaring as I approached the room she called her apartment. She was sitting as expected on the seat of her walker, leaning forward, eyeball-to-eyeball with the sports commentator. Her flowing cotton print dress was turquoise today with some canary yellow, lime green, and raspberry stitching on it. She looked like she was dressed for a Mexican vacation instead of another day in the old folks home.

"I'm glad you showed up today. I was thinking about you." Her voice was sandpaper, raspy and rough, just like the exterior she showed most of the world. Inside, Camellia was all cream puff. Her arms opened wide and wrapped me in a bear hug that squeezed the stiffness right out of my shoulders. "Now get in here and tell me what's going on with the Cowboys. Did they say Jerry Jones just fired the coach?"

"No, Camellia, I'm sure they didn't. I would have certainly heard news that big on the radio."

As I turned my attention to the television so I could translate what she had misunderstood, Camellia guided the walker to her recliner and plopped down. She did this quickly and gracefully in spite of her size and the fact she was constantly tethered to her oxygen concentrator. Without seeing the clear oxygen tube, she seemed to always be aware of it, at least enough to avoid getting tangled in it.

"You didn't happen to see what we're having for dinner as you came in?" Camellia asked. Age had not affected her appetite or her weight. Given her generous proportions and mine, it might not be a stretch for anyone to believe we really were mother and daughter.

"The menu said pork chops," I replied as I settled myself comfortably into the matching recliner next to hers, relieved that I had remembered to check the menu. Putting my feet up sounded much better than a trek back down the hall. "They said Jerry Jones just hired another assistant coach, not fired."

"Well that makes more sense. What are you fixing for supper tonight?"

"No clue. Maybe I'll just stay here and have a pork chop, and let Kevin fend for himself."

"That suits me just fine," she chuckled, no doubt thinking of the social coup of having her nurse, and reputed daughter, stay for dinner. "Naw, Kevin sounds like a good one. You should go on home and eat with him. Maybe pick up a pizza on the way so you don't have to cook. You don't need to be doing so much cooking since the kids are gone."

"I like to cook, Camellia, but you do have a point. While Andrew and Nicole were home for Christmas break, I probably cooked and washed dishes enough to last me for a while. Nicole had to have chicken tetrazzini, twice, and Andrew alternated his snacking between homemade salsa and Christmas cookies. I don't know how they stay so skinny."

As the conversation ebbed and flowed between sports and menus, the stress of all the traffic, the distraught families, the pressures of remembering everything everybody needed from me flowed away.

"Say, you take care of that lady across the hall?"

"Camellia, you know I'm not supposed to talk about other patients."

"Yeah, I know, but I hear you go in there sometimes."

I have always been a big fan of patient privacy. The Health Insurance Portability and Accountability Act has made it a crime for me to feel differently. I just have a devil of a time keeping my patients and families unaware of each other. When I visit patients in a facility, they all notice which rooms I go into, and when I see patients in my regular neighborhoods my car is often recognized.

"Anyway, the lady across the hall, Faye is her name, you should check on her before you leave today. I don't think she was feeling too good this afternoon."

"I will," I answered with an inward sigh. I could try to track the staff down to see if Faye was indeed having problems. However, the evening shift had come on duty at three o'clock, and Camellia might know something the current staff didn't. If I didn't check on her, Faye would cross my mind a thousand times tonight and I wouldn't rest until I was certain she was okay. Walking across the hall to check her blood pressure and listen to her lungs was no trouble. It was the accompanying three pages of paperwork that I dreaded.

"Well, I seem to have one more visit to make so I better get going," I said, bending over her to give and receive one more big hug.

"You ain't going to check my blood pressure today?"

"I don't need to unless you want me to. I've already checked it this week, and I'm trying to save some trees." A social visit was only a single page of documentation, a welcome relief to the forests of the world and my own battle with writer's cramp.

"Naw, I'm doing fine. I love you. Come back and see me when you can sit awhile."

"I will, Camellia. I love you, too," I called back as I paused at the door. I watched as she hunched over the walker with her normal stooped posture and pivoted back into place inches from the television screen. I could have held her arm while she moved to make sure she didn't fall, but that would qualify me as one of those jackasses she hated so much.

CHAPTER 11

Making another visit was the last thing I wanted to do. Thankfully there was no traffic involved, just a short walk across the hall from Camellia's room. It had been Camellia's suggestion that I check on Faye, and disregarding Camellia was always difficult to do. She had a way of getting her way. Based on my adopted status with Camellia it even seemed like disobedience to cross her.

As I entered Faye's room her back was to the door as usual. The blinds and curtains were open wide. She sat in a recliner facing the window, snuggled in a pile of pillows. Her room was homey. Misty, our hospice aide, made sure of that. She and some of the Ranch staff were always adding scented lotions and knickknacks from the dollar store to the rooms of their favorite patients. Even with those additions, Faye's room was sparse in comparison to Camellia's apartment. Camellia displayed a lifetime of memorabilia and treasures, while Faye had just a few trinkets and photos.

Faye didn't speak, but our entire team believed she was happy since her arrival at the Ranch. There seemed to be some contentment, even in her silence. She was no longer left in a chair for hours at a time, the room dark with no one stopping in to check on her. Now she was propped up comfortably with an assortment of pillows. Staff frequently stopped in to change her position in the chair, moving her to avoid bedsores and make her more comfortable. Even though she was unable to thank the aides for their kindness, they spoke to her. Each time they could be heard explaining their actions, "Faye, I'm going to move these pillows," or "Faye, I need you to drink some water for me."

She was hugged and sometimes kissed when they left. That may be how germs are spread, but it is definitely how love is spread. Love is very much worth such a small risk.

When she moved here and became my patient, we quickly discovered that her favorite activity was looking out the window. To vary her routine, sometimes her reclining chair equipped with wheels was moved to the activity room when singers were performing or when the other residents were playing bingo. Her dementia was far too advanced to hope for participation, but she could at least be there. Napping and looking were her only activities now.

As her mind rolled back in time to memories of her youth, her body rolled back its memory of how to function. She didn't remember how to walk or stand, but I had no doubt she remembered every detail of childhood. When I first met Faye, she could still speak occasionally, only a word or two here and there. The most she ever said to me was during a musical performance one day. She seemed to be visiting the present briefly, stirred to leave the past by the music. She was beaming with pride as she listened to a pretty young woman sing. Looking over at me, she said, "That's my granddaughter."

The Faye I know only has an elderly sister. Yet in that moment she had a granddaughter.

Today as I approached her chair, I began the usual one-sided chatter. "Hi, Faye. It's Linda, your nurse. I'm just here to take a quick peek at you. I'll try not to bother you too much. Those flowers outside sure are pretty."

Her window faced the courtyard, which always seemed to have some chaotic blooming going on, although from time to time, especially in the blazing heat of summer or cold of winter, the blossoms seemed to be of the plastic persuasion.

"I'm going to check your blood pressure. I promise it won't hurt," I said as I pumped up the cuff around her arm. I touched her shoulder, patted her hand, and continued to chat.

"That was perfect! I'm sure your blood pressure is better than mine. Now I'm going to listen to your heart and lungs."

Holding my stethoscope with my right hand to her chest, I rested my left hand on her shoulder while I listened. My biggest worry with dementia patients is lung sounds. Among the last functions to go is swallowing, and what doesn't go into the stomach goes into the lungs. It was a relief to hear nothing more than air moving. Faye and I could both rest peacefully tonight.

When I first spoke to her, she had looked in my direction, but her focus quickly returned to the window. She seemed unaware that I was still there despite my constant touching and ongoing conversation. "Faye, I don't know if you were feeling bad earlier today or not, but you seem fit as a fiddle to me." Bending over to interrupt her line of sight to the window, I gave her two thumbs up. "I'll make a quick note of this so I can leave a copy in your chart."

Pulling a three-page carbon note from my bag, I began hurriedly jotting down vital signs and checking boxes on each page. Lung sounds clear, thank goodness. Disoriented to person, place, and time. No evidence of pain. I continued my mindless chatter as I did the mindless paperwork. "I can smell dinner cooking. They'll be coming to take you to the dining room any minute. You're a lucky girl! It's pork chops tonight."

Faye's dinner would be pork chops just like everyone else

had, except it would be puréed to prevent choking, and fed to her by one of the staff. Continuing my monologue, I tucked her lap blanket around her legs and added, "I guess that's enough paperwork for now. You stay warm and have a good evening. I'm going to head back out into this blustery weather. Sorry I have to go. You know I'll be back soon. Good-bye, Faye."

Quickly, I crammed the yellow carbons in her plastic chart and fastened the originals to my clipboard. I bent down and gave her a quick peck on the forehead. Then, grabbing my blood pressure cuff, I headed for door. Another hug from Camellia would not fix my weariness now. I needed to get home. That pizza Camellia mentioned was sounding like a delicious, if not low-calorie, idea.

"You love your job, don't you?"

I froze in mid-step. I had made it almost to the doorway of Faye's room. Looking ahead into an empty hallway, I forced myself to breathe. No one was nearby, except Faye. It was definitely her voice I had heard. The sound had come from behind me, not the hall. Slowly, I retraced my steps, tossing my belongings into an empty chair. I dropped to my knees beside her. She looked at me now, ignoring the trees and plastic blooms outside her window. Our eyes met as I reached to hold her hand.

"Yes, ma'am. I do love my job."

Faye's dementia was cast aside, if just for a minute. She was with me now. Still looking into my eyes, she said simply, "I thought so."

Feeling humbled and honored at the same moment by the gift of her words, my breath caught in my throat. This time there was no room for doubt. She was looking into my eyes when she had spoken. Giving her hand a gentle squeeze, I said, "I love you, Faye."

A trace of a smile had crossed her lips when she spoke, which vanished as quickly as it came. With her hand still resting in mine, her eyes drifted back to the window. My gaze followed hers. No matter how hard I looked, I saw only smudged glass and fluttering fake flowers. Side by side, we looked directly ahead into two different worlds. Her mind had already journeyed back to days long ago. Looking from her face to the window, I wondered where she had gone. Was it to a sunny day running and giggling with friends somewhere in her childhood, or maybe just to the warmth of her mother's arms?

I stood slowly, and gave her another kiss on the forehead. "I'll be back to see you soon."

CHAPTER 12

July 1972

Mama can't use the little finger of her left hand. That doesn't sound like much of a problem, except she is left-handed. Since the Torino has power steering, she only drives with her left hand. She holds the steering wheel with it and uses just her little finger to flip the turn signal up and down. Or she did. She can't do it anymore.

She went to the doctor, so I know she is worried. Mama didn't even have a doctor of her own because she is never sick. She had to go to the doctor who Daddy went to before he died. Mama always said he was a good doctor, but he told her there was nothing wrong. He told her it was all in her head. My mother is not the type to become hysterical over losing her husband, especially almost two full years after his death. I hope that doctor knows medicine better than he knows my mother.

It's hard to believe, yet this month it really has been two whole years since Daddy died. I miss him, yet I don't think about him every minute of every day anymore. Mostly, I think about things he is missing. He doesn't know I can swim now. Daddy never let me take swimming lessons because he said I might drown. Last summer, Mama signed me up for swimming lessons, because she said if I could swim I was less likely to drown. Now I love the water. Sometimes when I go off the diving board, especially the high dive, I wish Daddy could see me.

Mama took me to see the GP rated movie *Love Story* with Ryan O'Neal and Ali MacGraw. I don't think Daddy would have ever let me see a GP movie, even if I was thirty years old. My aunts said Mama shouldn't have taken me, which made it even more fun. Mama didn't seem to think a curse word or two and a love scene was going to send me down the wrong path in life. Anyway, I didn't really understand the love scenes. I asked Mama what couples do in bed. She won't tell me. She just turned really red.

I should be able to see a movie like *Love Story*. After all, I am going into eighth grade in the fall. It will be my last year at Saint Leonard's before I start high school. And in less than six months, I will finally be a teenager. I'm growing, too. Already

I'm taller than Nina and Mama. Sometimes Mama and I stand back to back in front of her dresser mirror. Then we both turn our heads a little so we can see how much taller I am than she is. Even if it's not by much yet, I am the tallest person in the house. I wish Daddy could see.

The biggest change since Daddy died is not Mama's little finger or my growth spurt. It's Nina. She is confused a lot of the time. Mama doesn't let her cook anymore. She forgets when things like the stove or iron are hot, and Mama is afraid that either Nina will get burned or that she'll burn down the house. She has even turned on the gas to the stove, forgotten to light the burner, and walked away. Either Mama or I smell the gas and turn it back off. Mostly, Nina shuffles around the house in her tennis shoes like she's in a fog. She doesn't have much to say anymore, then out of the blue asks, "Where's Eddie?"

"He died, Nina. Daddy is dead. Don't you remember?" I answer, sometimes for the second or third time of the day if it's a bad day for her.

I get so tired of saying it. Then she looks sad and I feel guilty. I can't tell if she ever actually remembers his death, or if every time we answer her she feels the raw pain of hearing for the first time that her oldest son is gone. Either way, he was my daddy and Mama's husband, so it hurts us too, saying it over and over. It is such a strange thing to have to repeat. I think Mama is glad that it's summer, and when I'm not swimming

I'm home to look after Nina.

Mama finally got promoted at the plant. For nineteen years she has been an assembly line worker at General Electric. In my twelve years, I know she has never called in sick. She is never sick. She gets up at five fifteen every morning just so she can be early to work every day. Yet it took her nineteen years to get promoted. In the past, the bosses have always promoted only the men. The men are the primary breadwinners in their homes, so they say, and need a bigger paycheck. If those managers really believe that then I suppose they believe in Santa Claus and the Easter Bunny, too. And the moon is made of Swiss cheese.

All those years, Mama would have been a great foreman. Her daddy and brothers and sisters always depend on her, even though she is one of the youngest in her family. Whenever there is any kind of problem, Mama is the one who will solve it. Between her dependability and her leadership skills, General Electric would have been lucky to have her as a foreman.

Now, there's that darn little finger. Apparently, it is causing trouble with more than the turn signal. It's causing trouble with something she has to do at work with clothes dryer wiring harnesses. I don't really understand what she does at work, but I feel proud every time I put clothes in the dryer, just knowing that Mama made part of the machine.

Mama went back to the doctor. That's Mama. She knows there's something wrong, and she will just keep going back to that guy until he realizes that she was right all along. He really should listen to her. I'll bet the doctor wouldn't be happy if he could suddenly only use nine fingers instead of ten.

I've been worried, which is a fairly normal state for me. I worry about lots of different things, mostly school. I worry that I forgot to do my homework or that I got a wrong answer on a test. I always do my homework and hardly ever miss a test question. That doesn't stop me from worrying. Sometimes I think my grades are so good because the teachers take it for granted I did all my work, and that it's correct. Then I begin to worry that I'm not as smart as they seem to think I am, and that it's only a matter of time before the teachers figure it out.

So maybe worrying about a malfunctioning pinky finger doesn't seem so strange when I already worry about things that work fine. I just know that parents are only flesh and blood. Daddy's blood got too thick, or his heart had some kind of blockages, and he died. That makes me think something like that could happen to Mama, too. Death is not reserved only for old people.

CHAPTER 13

Pulling between two mountainous stone pillars, my Beetle chugged to a stop. Above me, a metal sign arched between the two pillars, proudly announcing the neighborhood's name. Attached to the pillar on my left was a glass and stone structure draped in a silver metal roof. The overall appearance of the guarded entry, intentionally and boastfully, screamed prestige and money. I shifted into first gear while waiting for the guard shuffling around inside to notice me. When at last he put down his cell phone and turned my way, he waved. The automatic gate squeaked once and swung open wide.

This neighborhood has been mine for a while now, territory our hospice automatically assigns to me. The first time I visited a patient in this community for seniors, I did her admission visit one day and her death visit the next. That was enough for the guard to recognize my car and decide I was not trying to breech his community's stone and metal fortress. When he was bored, his cell phone quiet, he would chat a moment as the gate slowly swung open. On my first visit, I had been obliged to state my business and intended address in order to gain admittance. Now Mr. Guard seemed to assume that was where I was headed each time. Unfortunately, I had now visited at least ten different addresses within his domain, these patients coming and going with only abbreviated hospice care.

I was more optimistic about my current patient here. Although the community was for "active seniors fifty-five and older," my patient at the moment was younger than me. He was the son of one of the property owners.

Jack had lived a charmed life. He was the all-American boy in a single package: handsome, intelligent, and well-educated. He graduated from college and landed his dream job, quickly becoming the star of the company. His college sweetheart was his soul mate, yet he never found the time to marry her. Life was just too busy, with Jack on a meteoric rise, jet setting around the country, making big deals and even bigger money. Around forty he encountered his first experience with failure, unfortunately in the form of his liver. Too many late nights drinking with clients, followed by too many supposedly harmless over the counter headache capsules in the morning left behind a falling star. When treatment was not viable, he became a young hospice patient.

Heading down the road from the pillared entryway to the gabled stone cottage where Jack lived with his mother, Betty, I found myself looking forward to our visit. Jack is a challenge. It is a challenge to keep him comfortable as his liver function decreases, but even more of a challenge to bring him comfort on a spiritual and emotional level. He has decreed that only I may visit, so I'm on my own to manage his care without help from Tom or Tricia, or even one of the aides. Our first encounter was rather hostile, so simply challenging is a definite improvement.

"Since I no longer have insurance, I'm paying privately for your services. I expect you here when I want you here, at my convenience," he had stated as an executive order.

Jack stands well over six feet tall and has perfected using his height as an advantage. He peered down at me, dark eyebrows furrowed, jaw set in a dare to disagree.

"I appreciate the fact that you are paying out of pocket for hospice care, however we do provide charity for the uninsured," I began.

"Charity? Charity? I do not accept charity," he boomed. "I paid for all my hospitalizations myself, in full. No one does that, but I did! I am not going to accept charity at this point in my life!"

"Fine, you can pay hospice for my nursing care. That still won't change my schedule. I normally have a caseload of between fourteen and eighteen patients and make five visits every day. I can't control traffic or how sick my other patients are, so I can't give you a definite appointment. Now, if you want to be my first visit of the day, I can be more consistent…"

"You will not visit in the morning, and I will tell you what time you are coming!"

I really love my patients, but misplaced anger can be a bitch. I took a calming breath so deep my chest stretched tight. Exhaling slowly, I added what I hoped was a large serving of honey to my already slow Southern drawl. I said, "As you wish. You may tell me what time I am to arrive."

"You will agree to an appointment then?" There was a twinge of victory in his voice, diluting the anger. His eyebrows relaxed as his jaw unclenched, at least slightly. Jack was a man who had been in control of everything. Now he found himself in control of nothing, including his very life. That justified his need to control my schedule, even if it didn't make it practical.

"Yes, you may have any appointment time you wish," I said smiling. "Of course, when I agree to it, I will be lying. No matter what I agree to do, I still will not be able to control the traffic, how much time my other patients need, and of course, random emergency calls. The most specific appointment choices I can reasonably give are morning, early afternoon, or late afternoon. If changes come up, I call." If looks could kill, I would have been dead before anyone could have put me on hospice.

He had not thrown me out that first day. That was a very good sign. If anything, he possibly respected me for not backing down. It was a quality he was not accustomed to confronting in others, but something he appreciated in himself. Besides, I was right, and he knew it.

As I parked on the sloping driveway, and pulled the emergency brake on, I couldn't help but wonder what today would bring. My visits with Jack were usually about two hours, much longer than I stayed with most patients. Patients often tire easily and some are unresponsive. Jack, on the other hand, seemed to enjoy having someone from his decade to debate with. His favorite topic quite naturally was death, with his own lurking around the corner.

"Hi, Betty," I said as the door opened on my first knock.

"Come in, Linda. It's so good to see you."

She wrapped her arms around me before I completely crossed the threshold, giving me a quick kiss on the cheek at the same time. She had a broad navy bow tied neatly in her blonde-white hair. The hair ribbon matched her suit, and of course coordinated with her shoes, and most likely a purse. As always, she was country club dressed, ready for either a garden club meeting or a ladies' luncheon. Her stylish appearance and immaculately coiffed hair give her an air of quiet sophistication. The suffering and turmoil of her life have no visible presence. It's as if the peace in her soul will not allow it.

"How are you feeling today, Betty?" I asked with genuine concern. I care equally for Betty and Jack. Losing a child is too gut wrenching to comprehend. Andrew and Nicole might both be in college now, but they are still my babies. I can't even consider anything happening to either one of them while I am alive. Betty is caring for a son on hospice. Jack will be the second child she has buried. Another son, her Andrew, was killed as a young boy.

"I'm doing just fine. Thanks for asking. Jack? Where are you? Linda is here. Don't keep her waiting."

"Back here," he called from the family room.

"Hi there, Jack," I said entering the comfortably decorated room. Richly upholstered chairs sat on either side of a sofa. The coffee table, end tables, and a writing desk were of cherry, polished to a near mirror gloss. The family room was cheerfully illuminated by a wall of windows and French doors at the back, giving a floor-to-ceiling view of park-like grounds. To the left, the sitting area was bordered by an expansive granite bar, opening to the kitchen. Like its owner, the house never had a hair out of place, yet exuded a warm welcome.

"Don't get up," I added as he grabbed the arm of the sofa

in a preliminary attempt to hoist himself up. "Your feet are really swollen today. Stay where you are, just let me slide this ottoman under your legs to elevate them."

"I told him that," Betty said sternly. "He doesn't listen to his mother. Maybe he will listen to his nurse."

"Mom, I told you, it doesn't help," Jack said as he let me slide the ottoman into place.

"Gravity is gravity," I said pushing my thumb against his swollen lower leg to assess the degree of edema. "It will take a medication change to solve the problem. In the meantime, keep those water balloons you call feet off the floor."

"Aye, aye, Captain," he replied with a quick salute and a grin.

"Don't be so sassy, young man," Betty replied as the phone began ringing. "Now where did I leave that darn telephone? It sounds like it's coming from my bedroom. If you'll excuse me."

As Betty left the room, Jack did his best to spring to his feet. "Come on. Let's go outside before she gets back."

Like naughty children, we went silently and as quickly as he was able through the French doors to a covered patio. He lowered himself to a white wicker couch, with no complaints uttered when I pointed at his feet and the other side of the couch. As Jack situated himself on the pink floral cushions, feet up, I took a seat in the matching wicker rocker.

"Mom means well, and I don't know what I'd do without

her," he began. "There's just no privacy with her around."

"I know. She is worried about you," I said, trying not to imagine myself in Betty's position. It was too horrible.

"Are you worried about me?"

"I don't like the way the swelling looks; however, I don't think it's anything we can't fix. Maybe fix isn't the right word. Let's say that Dr. Kazi will give orders that will make it significantly better."

"I know the routine. You'll change my diuretics, send the new pills via FedEx, and make triple sure I understand the dose and directions. That's not what I meant. Do you ever worry about what happens next?"

"No, I wouldn't say I worry. I think good people end up in a good place, and evil people end up in hell. I've told you that. I also believe in goodness, and that there is more good than bad in almost everyone."

"Mom worries that I don't go to church," he continued. "I don't have anything against the church. I'm just not as Catholic as she is."

"Neither is the pope!"

Jack laughed. Happiness looked good on him, much better than the anger that had contorted his face a month or so ago on the day we met. "I can't imagine what it will be like."

"Actually, I think you will be able to do more than just imagine it before you go. Most people don't die suddenly, in car and plane crashes, or in their sleep from heart attacks. Everyone wants to believe that is how their end will be, but what is happening to you is much more likely," I said.

"I would never have imagined myself on hospice, taking all these medications, unable to get anything except house slippers on these gigantic feet."

"No one wants to suffer."

"I'm uncomfortable sometimes. I wouldn't actually call it suffering. You and your pills for this and pills for that…"

"You wouldn't even have to be uncomfortable if you took those pills like you're supposed to," I interjected.

"Yeah, I know I could take more pain medication. Remember, you won't let me take it if I'm driving, and I have to get out of the house sometimes."

"I know, and I appreciate the fact you don't put the entire county at risk by taking pain killers and driving. As I was saying, when you get closer to the end you seem to experience the other side, heaven, at least to a degree. I feel like my patients move back and forth between heaven and earth. Unless you die suddenly, your soul or spirit, whatever you want to call it, seems to be able to hover between both worlds for a while."

"I've heard your stories. I just hope you're right."

"Me too. My patients just about have me convinced that it happens that way. It's like I always tell you, I'm just here to be your guide on this journey. Since I obviously haven't made the trip, I can only tell you what my patients have experienced."

"So, you honestly believe death isn't that sudden, or doesn't happen all at once? I thought when my liver finally fails, I'll just be gone."

"That's still not like the sudden death of a heart attack or accident. I had one patient in a coma for a couple of days. I really thought he would die without ever waking back up. He did wake up briefly, however, and when he did he told his wife where he had been. He said that he had been with their grandchildren. One had died as a toddler, drowned in a pool. The other was a granddaughter who died as a teenager in a car crash. This family had experienced so much loss, yet they handled my patient's death beautifully. His wife said she couldn't have asked for more than to have him tell her where he was going and who he would be with. He even told her she wouldn't join him there for a long time, because she needed to stay behind for their children and other grandchildren."

"That makes sense, possibly because I just want to believe you. I can't talk about this with Mom. She seems so sure of purgatory and all the other catechism she has been taught."

"Yeah, well, we all have our own beliefs…"

"That's just it. I prefer to develop my own beliefs than recite medieval catechism. You still go to church, though. Mom says she sees you and your husband there."

"I do go to Mass. It's not that I think the church has it all figured out, but I need some spiritual guidance."

The French doors swung open, signaling an end to the day's ethereal musings. "There you are! Why are we sitting outside today? The wind is chilly," Betty said as she stepped out the door. "I'm sorry I was on the phone so long. Some people just won't stop talking."

"Fine, Mom. We'll go back inside. Linda has just been cooped up all day, so I told her we could sit out here."

"I just love your yard, Betty," I added for support.

"Thank you, but it's entirely too cool for Jack to be out here," she said, holding the door open, ushering the petulant children back inside.

Leaving the spiritual contemplation to be carried away on the breeze, our visit quietly settled back into the realm of nursing and factual assessments. With Jack once again seated, feet up, I began by listening to his heart and lungs. The regular thumping of his heart and deep breathing were a change from the hearts and lungs of patients twice his age that I usually listen to. Like his heart rate, his blood pressure was textbook normal. "Your blood pressure is very good, Jack," I said as I pulled my stethoscope from my ears.

"That's wonderful," Betty exclaimed.

I knew that at her age hypertension was often a concern. Hearing that Jack's blood pressure was normal would reassure her, which was my intention. Looking at his gradually yellowing skin and his swelling was enough to cause her panic. She needed something to be normal, even if it wasn't pertinent to his condition.

"Let me double check with Dr. Kazi on changing your dose of furosemide. Normally, we would increase it by giving you two pills every morning instead of one. Since your liver is the problem, we have to be very careful. It functions as a filter for your body, and we don't want to make it work too hard." Looking down at my cell phone, I frowned at it, adding, "Betty, I'm just going to step outside and enjoy that yard again while I call Dr. Kazi. I think I will have better phone reception out there than I do inside."

"Please just use my house phone then," she said handing me the handset she was still carrying from her earlier call.

"No, thank you, although I appreciate the offer. Since I'm calling the doctor's cell phone, which has Caller ID, he won't answer unless he recognizes my number."

"I see. Well, we will wait right here." Betty had settled herself in the chair closest to Jack.

As I stepped back out the French doors he gave me a look that said, "You might have fooled Mom, but you didn't fool me."

"Dr. Kazi, this will be quick," I said glancing at Betty, willing her to stay inside. "I'm with Jack…"

"The young man with liver failure. Yes, Linda, go on."

Bless Dr. Kazi and his amazing memory. "Jack has four plus pitting edema, bilaterally in his lower extremities…"

"Any jaundice?"

"Yes, but his skin doesn't seem to be itching from it yet."

The conversation was brief as expected, while it touched on all the changes Jack was experiencing, the changes he could feel, and Betty could see. Once inside, I would relay the information with the cold clinical words removed, and hopefully the fear along with them.

Slipping back inside I said, "Jack, Dr. Kazi said you are to keep your feet up as much as possible. Gravity is not your friend."

"You heard her, Jack," Betty added. "Feet up! That means no driving."

Jack pleaded with his eyes.

"Now, Betty, that's not what I said. I said as much as possible, not non-stop. Besides, tomorrow morning Jack, you will take two of your diuretics instead of one, and these legs will hopefully deflate some. In the meantime, Betty, you need to put a bath towel under his legs, on top of the ottoman."

"Sure, I can do that," she said popping up from her chair, obviously glad to have a concrete task to perform.

"Why a towel?" he asked as she left the room.

"Well, Jack, your legs may begin to weep. When I pushed on them it took a long time for the pitted mark my thumb made in your leg to disappear. We call that four plus pitting edema. The next step is weeping edema, with the fluid coming out of your legs through your skin."

"I see," he said simply, and I knew he did.

"Here's the towel," Betty said as she returned with a thick navy towel. "Now what am I watching for?" she asked, putting the towel down as directed.

"The fluid may come out of his legs. That will just catch it," I said.

"Well, I suppose it has to come out one way or the other," Betty replied, the tranquility in her voice mirroring my own.

"I'm calling in additional pills, because now that you are taking two every morning, you will run out faster. I'm also sending another drug Dr. Kazi suggested. It is called Atarax. Don't worry about it now. It's one of those things we like to have on hand just in case we need it. You know how anything that goes wrong seems to happen in the middle of the night, usually on a Sunday or holiday. Nothing ever goes wrong when your neighborhood pharmacy is open."

"That's the truth," Betty agreed.

"Atarax is for?" Jack asked.

"Itching. Sometimes it's a problem when your skin is jaundiced. The toxins not being excreted by your liver come out through your skin. It can begin to itch, and if it does you will be thrilled to have the Atarax here. Who knows, maybe we will prevent the symptom by having the medication on hand."

As I gathered my clipboard, car keys, and blood pressure cuff to leave, Betty rose from her chair again. "Jack, feet up, no complaining. I'm going to walk Linda to her car."

"See you next week," he said.

"Actually, I'd like to pop back in this week to check on the swelling if you don't mind."

"No, I don't need another visit. Save it for the sick people," Jack said smiling. "Besides, if anything changes Nurse Betty here will give you a call."

"See you next week then," I said, turning to leave with Betty shadowing me.

"How bad is it?" she asked as soon as we were out the front door.

"He is sick. I honestly don't know, Betty. I've told Jack this already, you can live as long without your liver as you can without your heart."

"You can't..." she began.

"That's right," I said, holding her arm for support. Even with the harsh reality we were discussing, she never wavered. She had turned to face me, her blue eyes staring into mine and into the truth. "His liver is still working, some. Eventually it will just fail."

"I know," she said. "Is there anything else I can do for him?"

Bolstered by her courage, I found some of my own. "Well,

Betty, there is one thing you could do. When I visit, Jack likes to discuss what is going to happen next..."

"His death you mean," she said directly, using the word I had tried to side step and dance around.

"Yes, he wants to discuss his death. More specifically, he wants to discuss what might happen after death. I believe he would be more comfortable having these conversations one on one." I paused waiting for her reaction.

"Don't be silly. Jack and I are very close. He wants me there. We are very close," she repeated. "There is nothing he can't and won't say in front of me."

"You are close, however..."

"Besides, there is nothing along those lines to discuss. Jack will go to heaven when he dies. He knows exactly what happens. He was raised Catholic, even if he doesn't go to church now."

"Sure, Betty," I said, admitting defeat. "Call me if you need anything, and watch for the medications to be delivered in the morning."

I watched her wave good-bye in my rear view mirror as I headed down the street. Mentally, I disagreed with her, but because I have a son too, my heart understood every word.

CHAPTER 14

August 1972

Finally, after a few more visits, the doctor believed Mama. I'm glad for her. She was frustrated when she couldn't get him to listen. Now I'm past worried. I'm scared. They have "exploratory brain surgery" scheduled for the beginning of August. Exploratory is a word used by NASA when they are searching outer space. It is very uncomfortable to have a doctor use that word. I would rather have him know what he was looking for than go searching the depths of Mama's brain for something.

The day before the surgery, Mama and I walked up the stone steps of the hospital hand in hand. I didn't pull away, because at that moment, I didn't feel much like an almost teenager.

With my right hand, I clutched Mama's small suitcase, which I liked to think of as an overnight bag. That made it sound like she would be back home soon. We passed through the two-story columns, leaving the heat and humidity behind. The lobby smelled of cool air and disinfectant. A doctor's name crackled across the loudspeaker, paging him to return to the third floor nurses' station. Mama and I followed the signs to the admissions desk.

Mama signed in and we slid together onto a blue vinyl couch. "Daddy was never in this hospital," I chattered nervously. "You and I were both patients here when I was born."

"That's right," Mama answered. "The only time your father ever left the house without combing his hair was the night he drove me here to the hospital to have you. While you were being born, he was trying to buy a comb in the gift shop so he wouldn't meet you with messy hair."

"I never saw his hair messed up."

"Georgia Bauer?" the lady behind the desk called.

"It's Georgie, spelled with an ie," Mama answered as we stood up, and walked toward the admission lady.

The lady looked over the top of her glasses at me in disapproval. "Children must be twelve to go upstairs, you know."

"Yes, I know," Mama answered crisply as she slid her insurance card across the desk.

"And Mr. Bauer?" the dense lady persisted.

"Yes?"

Mama might be a patient, but she was still Mama.

"Well, it is most unusual for a child to accompany a patient to the hospital," the lady answered, still glaring in my direction.

"Yes, well, Linda is most unusual for a twelve-year-old child. Mr. Bauer is deceased. Linda is with me today, and I am very lucky to have her. What room did you say I am in?"

A candy stripe volunteer appeared pushing a wheelchair. She was a real teenager wearing a pink and white striped apron over a white uniform dress. "Let me help you," she was saying to Mama.

"Why, thank you," Mama answered, taking a seat before the volunteer had a chance to help. She pushed Mama in the wheelchair while my shoes tapped across the shiny floor to the elevator. I smiled. Mama was still in charge of the world, and we were very lucky to have each other.

I set my clock to get up early the next morning. I dressed quickly, and pulled my hair back in a ponytail. "Nina, I'm leaving," I said, giving her a quick peck on the cheek.

"Where are you going? School?" she asked, managing to look disappointed and a little confused at the same time.

"It's summer," I answered, exasperated that she could forget the gravity of the day that had my stomach tied neatly into knots. "I'm not even wearing my school uniform. How could

I be going to school? Mama is having surgery today, and I'm going to wait at the hospital. Aunt Shirley and Aunt Thelma are picking me up. I've told you this a dozen times."

Patting my hip pocket, I checked for the third or fourth time that I had the money Mama had given me to buy lunch in the hospital cafeteria and my house key. I needed to lock the door behind me. Nina might not hear me knock when I came home, or figure out that she needed to open the door. Without another backward glance at Nina, I went out on the front porch to wait for my ride.

The smell of disinfectant again met me at the hospital front door. It was just like yesterday, except today I was tagging behind my aunts with my hands swinging free at my sides. They talked to each other, not so much to me. The loudspeaker crackled its greeting, paging first one person then another. Nurses bustled past in their ghostly garb of white dresses, stockings, shoes, and caps. They all looked alike, except some of the caps were shaped a bit different. It felt like I'd stumbled onto the set of *Marcus Welby, M.D.*

"Georgie with a bald head. I can't imagine it."

"She has such thick, pretty hair."

"It has, or had, such a nice curl."

My aunts were still lamenting the loss of my mother's hair as the elevator groaned its way upstairs. I had given up on joining in their conversation, realizing I would get more information if

I kept quiet and let them forget I was still listening.

"I wish we could have seen her before they took her into surgery."

"Not with that bald head, I don't."

I tried to close my eyes and imagine Mama without hair, but I couldn't do it. Uncle Frederick had been almost bald. Otherwise, I couldn't think of any bald people. I had always liked Uncle Frederick, Nina's baby brother, but Mama bore no resemblance to a skinny old man with wire rim glasses. Mama was a pretty lady with green eyes, dark curly hair, and lipstick. A shaved head with lipstick was too much even for my imagination. Shaved head or not, I wanted to see her, and the sooner the better.

We arrived at Mama's hospital room, now just a hollow space without her. We stood around for a moment, none of us knowing quite what to do next. We needed Mama to guide us.

"If you're waiting for Mrs. Bauer, you can go to the surgery waiting area. The doctor will come out and talk to you there as soon as she is in recovery." One of the white dressed clones had appeared before us, ready to show us to the waiting area. We followed silently down the hall behind her, a million questions hanging in the air, but none that we really wanted to ask.

There were more vinyl couches and chairs in here, some a dingy army green, some blue, as if someone had started to redecorate and decided it wasn't worth the effort. A black and white television broadcasting either a summer snow shower or a poorly received television show played in the corner.

"I'm going to the cafeteria now," I said before we had chosen our favorite color of vinyl seats.

"Now?" Aunt Shirley and Aunt Thelma chimed together.

"Yes. I want to get back before the doctor comes out to talk to us. If I don't go now, and the surgery is over early, I might miss him."

The cafeteria was deserted, too late for breakfast, too early for lunch. I slid into a booth as a waitress handed me a menu and set a glass of water before me. Like everyone else in the hospital, she was wearing a uniform. Hers was pink with a matching ruffled hat bobby pinned into her beehive hair instead of the nurses' white caps with black stripes.

"You by yourself, honey?"

"Yes, ma'am," I answered. She arched one dark penciled eyebrow at me, so I added, "Mama gave me money to eat while she is in the operating room."

"Where's your daddy? Upstairs waiting on your mom?"

"He died," I said looking at her over the top of the plastic menu. I have had to say that a lot in the past two years to a number of strangers, and of course, repeatedly to Nina. My voice doesn't quiver anymore when I say Daddy is dead. I say it like my phone number or address or any other piece of information. I can anticipate the response, also. There is a look of concern, quickly overshadowed by morbid curiosity that leads to the follow-up question. There are two variations to the question actually. The first is simply, "How did he die?" The waitress opted for the other choice.

"Car crash?"

"Heart attack."

"Oh dear! You poor little thing," she gushed.

"I'll have a chocolate shake, plain hamburger, and an order of fries."

"What? Oh, your order! Now you want that burger dressed or with some cheese? Maybe mustard?"

"Just plain, please."

"Right, honey," she said, scrawling something on her order pad that I hoped included the word plain. "Poor little thing," she continued muttering as she walked away with my menu.

In a few minutes I noticed her talking to the other waitress and nodding in my direction. Mama and I have been pretty happy together. I wish the world would quit treating me like Little Orphan Annie just because Daddy died. The waitresses continued nodding and frowning toward me while I waited for my order. I didn't need to hear their words to understand the conversation they were having about me. At the moment I was very glad I hadn't mentioned that Mama was having brain surgery.

My favorite meal is a plain hamburger, French fries, and

chocolate milkshake. That is what I always eat when I get the chance. Every waitress always wants to dress my burger, putting disgusting things like mustard, pickles, or onions on it. I never let them. I don't want anything to come between the meat and bread to hide the flavor. Today, however, while I wait for Mama to come out of surgery I could have ordered wet paper towels with a side of cardboard, and enjoyed it just as much, or as little. The only flavor I tasted was fear. I had hoped eating would kill some time, but the coffee shop wasn't busy so service was disappointingly fast. At least the waitresses were filling the salt and pepper shakers now instead of discussing my fate.

My stomach hurt as I slurped the last of my milkshake through the straw. I always like it when they serve the milkshake in a tall glass with whipped cream and bring the silver tumbler they made it in with the leftover shake. Today, I would have exploded if I had to take another sip. I didn't really want any of it, but I could hear Mama and the nuns talking about starving children in Africa. This was not the moment to be wasteful.

Still lost in my thoughts, I looked down at the check and realized that unless I could choke a piece of cake or pie down to add to my tab, my cafeteria reprieve was coming to an end. After my waitress laid the bill on the edge of the table she resumed her duties, now putting out fresh yellow and red plastic squirt bottles of mustard and ketchup in anticipation of the lunch crowd. She managed to do that chore while sneaking frequent glances in my direction. My cheeks burned red under her gaze. Daddy is dead, and Mama is having brain surgery. I can't change either one of those facts. Still, looks of pity embarrass me. I feel that I did something wrong somehow, just because my life has turned in a different direction.

Pulling out my wrinkled money to pay, I mumbled my thanks and good-byes and headed toward the gift shop. I didn't really have a plan for waiting out Mama's surgery beyond the hamburger in the cafeteria. The gift shop seemed like the perfect solution. That perfection lasted about a minute and a half. It was a closet-sized space, stocked primarily with flower drenched get-well cards and pastel colored baby gifts.

Slowly, I began wandering the shiny-floored hallways. The too-clean smell of disinfectant still hung in the air. With nowhere to go, no place to be, I tried to walk slowly enough to waste time and quickly enough to avoid appearing lost. When the doctor visited Mama's room yesterday evening he said I am supposed to wait a couple of hours for her to get out of surgery and go into recovery. I didn't ask exactly what that meant, but I think I know from television. The doctor, who will be wearing a scrub suit and mask, should come through a swinging set of doors and tell me she's just fine and I can see her in a little while. Or not.

It was definitely better to wait alone than with the aunts. I was sure they were still dwelling on Mama as a bald person, not my favorite topic. My sister should be here. I sometimes imagined her as someone who liked me, who did family things. Mama always says I have a terrific imagination. My sister, however, didn't seem to like me much, and definitely didn't go to hospitals, or funeral homes, even when Daddy died. She was more the mall or movie theater type of sister.

Yesterday, Mama and I had passed a sign pointing the way to the hospital chapel. My slow moving feet carried me in that direction now. Finding myself in front of the chapel door, I decided to wait out the brain exploration there. Since my sister didn't do church either, I knew she wouldn't have waited in the chapel with me.

The chapel was dark and cool with the fluorescent glare of the hospital thankfully absent. A pair of stain-glassed lanterns cast a dim glow. Sitting on a small wooden table, a single candle burned inside a ruby red cylinder. I slid into the front pew and lowered myself onto a padded leather kneeler. No one else was here. I hoped God was.

Silently, I began praying the Our Father. The second time through the prayer, my eyes wandered to my wristwatch. It was the Timex Daddy had bought for my seventh birthday just after he had gotten out of the hospital.

I held the watch up to my ear and listened to it tick. There wasn't another sound in the chapel. The hospital loudspeaker croaking names into the air could have been a million miles away. There were no aunts rattling on about shaved heads. There were no televisions broadcasting crackling commercials and soap operas. I listened to the silence and thought about Daddy. Could he see me? Was he like an angel watching over me? Watching over Mama? I hoped so. "Daddy, if you're listening, Mama misses you so much. She acts very brave, and she is brave. Still, I know how much she misses you. You just can't have her yet. I need her here."

I looked back at my watch. The hands didn't seem to be moving, so I checked the stem. It was pushed in and wound tight. The tick, tick, tick continued. Time was moving, just not inside this chapel. "I won't look at my wristwatch for five minutes," I told myself and tried to pray again.

When I go to confession, the priest always has me say prayers for penance. One Our Father seems to be the going rate of penance for telling a lie. How many Our Fathers would I have to pray for Mama to be okay? The priest probably doesn't even know the answer to that. I should have brought a rosary with me to help me focus on the prayers and to keep count of how many I pray.

Two minutes. So much for waiting at least five minutes between glances at my watch.

My attempted prayers, woven tightly with worries, continued. What if Mama wasn't okay? Could she die during surgery? That happens sometimes on television shows. I tried harder to pray, but all that came out was, "Hail Mary full of grace, what do the doctors expect to find inside Mama's brain?"

As time crawled past, I stayed on my knees. Would this hurt Mama? Would she have a terrible headache when she woke up? What if she didn't wake up? Even with thick padding on the kneeler, after a while I couldn't feel my knees anymore. The only thing I could feel was the pit of my stomach.

By the time I returned to the surgery waiting room, fear had silenced my aunts. After praying and then sitting on an ugly vinyl couch for several hours, I knew. The doctor who hadn't believed Mama believed her now.

Eventually, just like on television, the metal doors of the surgical area swung open. The doctor emerged, giving words to that pain still growing in the pit of my stomach. "Your mother has a brain tumor, and she's going to die. We think she has about six months left to live, but we're not going to tell her. We will tell her that we removed the tumor and she will get well. This will make her feel better. Do you understand? You can never tell her she's dying."

The next moment I was in the elevator with my aunts standing around me. The bells announcing the next floor were drowned by my shrieks. A woman got on at one of the stops and Aunt Thelma apologized for me. "Her daddy is dead, and she just found out her mama is dying, too."

I shrieked louder.

CHAPTER 15

Visiting Bonnie soon became one of the highlights of my week. Thanks to Mama, I have a soft spot in my heart for bald women. Passing through the now familiar curved lanes of the mobile home park, I watched for the first signs of spring. I was looking forward to thick shade trees, especially here. The green would soften the stark metal of the homes, and maybe make Bonnie feel a little more like she was back on the front porch of the home she and Jim had given up. I tried to believe Bonnie would not be gone before the early arrival of Texas summer.

Experience, however, had taught me that a doctor's promise of six months and six months on a calendar were often unrelated. Now if I could just teach that hard-earned lesson.

Recently, I failed spectacularly at imparting that particular bit of information. It started with a page to call Bonnie's daughter.

"Hi, Rachel. Is Bonnie okay?" I had asked, unable to hide my concern.

"Yeah, she's fine. Why wouldn't she be?" came the cool breeze of response.

Well, she is dying of cancer I thought, but said, "How can I help you? The office paged me that you had called."

"It's nothing, really. My husband and I booked a cruise for next month. The tickets are non-refundable, so I just want to be sure there's not a problem."

"Rachel, if you are asking me if your mother will still be with us a month from now, I don't know. I can't answer that."

"The tickets are non-refundable," she repeated more slowly in an obvious attempt to match the speed of my thought processes. "We need you to know so that she is fine until we get back."

"Are you saying you already booked the cruise?"

"Yes, twice so far I have told you we booked a cruise."

Her indignation at my stupidity was only exceeded by her own lack of mental capacity. It wasn't uncommon for patients and families to schedule events beyond the anticipated time of death. It was denial written in ink on a calendar. Father always likes baseball, so we bought season tickets. We're taking Mother to the family reunion in the spring. If we have it scheduled, it will happen. Rachel had not invented the concept. She was just adding a dash of nasty to it.

"Rachel, your mother is terminal, and she is declining. The timing of her death is not up to me."

"We return on the ninth. Make sure she is okay until then. I really need to get away, and this will be just perfect."

"I have serious doubts that your mother will still be with us on the ninth of next month…" I attempted to explain. Quickly I realized I was talking to myself. Rachel had issued her mandate and hung up.

Rachel wouldn't enjoy the trip. In spite of her rudeness, she cared for her mother, and thoughts of her would be a constant companion even at sea. If she had asked, I would have told her to take a trip after her mother passed and to spend as much time with Bonnie as possible now while she could. Then she could go on vacation, taking those warm, consoling memories along. It's just hard to help someone see the light of day when their misconceptions are closed so darkly around them.

I tried to banish the recent unpleasantness with Rachel from my mind as I got out of my car. Jim was watching for me at the door as usual. The General now greeted me with a genuine smile, unshed tears no longer sparkling in his eyes. "She's waiting for you," he said as he held open the storm door.

My presence appeared to reassure him. At first I had called to ask if I could visit. Now I still called before I came, but just said I was on my way, with a guesstimate of my arrival time. If I had called at five or six in the morning saying I was in the area, Jim would probably let me stop by.

As I entered the room, Bonnie was hanging up the phone. Propped on pillows with the head of the bed elevated, she looked ready to give orders, even to the General. "I'm glad you're here today."

She moved her shoulders slightly toward me and I was drawn by gravity, or magnetism, or maybe just love, straight to her. I bent to give her a hug. Her yellow cotton nightgown was soft in contrast to the bony frame underneath it. "How are you feeling?"

"I'm fine, but Jim's not," she responded with a silencing look in his direction.

His smile had faded with her comment. He looked at his shoe tops and did not argue with her. I saw fatigue in his face, but that was to be expected. The living area appeared in order, as did the kitchen. A few dishes were in the drainer. The countertops glistened with everything in place. Caring for an invalid twenty-four hours a day and keeping up with even a small mobile home was a monumental task. If Jim was struggling with it, there were no visible clues.

"Why don't you tell me what's going on," I said as I sat in the plaid upholstered chair next to Bonnie's bedside. Beau looked up from beneath Bonnie's bed, but decided I was neither new nor interesting, and quickly went back to sleep.

"Well, the kids," she hesitated, as if deciding how to proceed. "They have their own lives, and we knew they wouldn't be much help. They stop by, but Jim has to do everything by himself, cooking, cleaning, caring for me, and it's quite simply wearing him down."

Jim had settled into his usual spot, a kitchen chair placed on the other side of Bonnie's bed. He still looked uncomfortable. It was likely the first time in his life he needed help.

"Who wouldn't need help?" I asked. "Of course, adult children are still your children. You don't want to burden them. Besides, I am sure they are busy with their own families."

The lie slipped easily from my mouth, although I had vigorously promised Bonnie honesty. It just seemed appropriate at the moment to defend Jim and Bonnie's feelings, which meant defending their children. Knowing their daughter Rachel was taking a cruise rather than helping her parents made the lie a slightly bitter pill to swallow, but I managed. Besides, it certainly wasn't the first time a family hadn't pulled together in a crisis. Immediate family members of my patients, both children and siblings, are not infrequently absent from the bedside.

Sometimes the reason for the absence is glaring. The patient, or more often their spouse, may be unwelcoming. A few have gone way past unwelcoming and been so cantankerous that I had to force myself to drive in their direction even though I am getting paid to visit. No one, blood-related or not, would voluntarily visit those patients. Other times, the reason is not as apparent. There just may be long ago wounds that damaged the relationship and have never healed.

In Bonnie and Jim's case, none of that applied. The children seemed to love them both. Yet they never visited long, and certainly not long enough to help. They were always on their way somewhere more important, with only a minute to spare. A place more important than their dying mother's bedside was not a location I could grasp.

"Do you know what kind of time frame we are looking at? I can manage, at least for a while longer," Jim asked quietly.

"I still don't have a crystal ball; however, it's been my experience that you can project how things are going to progress by what has happened so far. Bonnie, you were walking, and now you are bedbound. How quickly did that happen?"

"Pretty quick. It seems like overnight."

Jim and Bonnie thought about what I was predicting. "I don't think I have long either," Bonnie said with courage I can't comprehend. "I always thought the doctor was lying about me having six months. Jim still needs some help."

"We were thinking about having my brother and sister-in-law come stay. The trailer is pretty small, so we don't want to invite them if it's going to be months," Jim said, waiting for my agreement that it would indeed be a few more months before Bonnie left him.

"Bonnie, you seem to think it's a good idea, and Jim, the patients always know more about these things than I do. They even seem to have some control over it." My first thought was of Mike and his business deal that had to go through. It was just a little too fresh to talk about yet.

"You really think so?" Bonnie had brightened at the thought of having control over something again.

"Did I ever tell you about my patient named Tiny? She taught me how much patients really know about when they are going."

"I don't remember you ever mentioning her," Bonnie said. She was sitting up in bed, arms wrapped around her bent knees, like a child waiting for a bedtime story.

I collected my thoughts, hoping to give Bonnie and Jim some encouragement. "Tiny's family described her as a whirlwind, but by the day we met, Tiny was already confined to her bed. She was declining quickly, and soon the day came when she couldn't even eat or drink. Her daughter Karen was medically trained and refused the extra help hospice could send."

"You've talked about Continuous Care," Jim interjected. "I'm not so sure I'd want to try to squeeze more people, especially strangers, into our house."

"It's not for everybody, and Tiny's family didn't want it either. Anyway, about three days passed and Karen asked me to stop by. When I got there, Tiny was staring at the ceiling in the corner of her room."

I thought about Tiny at that moment. She had had a look of peace on her face that defied earthly description. The only thing that came to mind was the look of love a new mother has on her face when she sees her baby for the first time. Clearing my throat, my voice cracked with the memory. "Karen explained that Tiny had been staring like that for almost the entire three days since my last visit. Leaning close to Tiny I just had to ask if she was looking at heaven. To my surprise, and her daughter's, she looked away from the ceiling and into my eyes. She didn't speak right away. Perhaps she was trying to determine what portion of her experience she could share. Karen and I were after all still mere mortals, with limited powers of comprehension."

I felt tears building in my eyes at the memory and paused just long enough to fight them back. Bonnie and Jim were in desperate need of hope and answers, not tears at the moment.

After a moment I continued, "Looking in my eyes, Tiny told me that not only was she seeing heaven, she was going there that very night. And when she got there she was going dancing. She then looked back up at the ceiling, letting Karen and I know our lesson on heaven was over."

"But it wasn't?" Bonnie asked, with hope in her voice.

"No, it wasn't," I said. "With my days spent talking to patients and families, I usually enjoy quiet in the evenings. However, that night at home, my daughter Nicole and I were painting my bedroom. We had the radio playing, half dancing, half singing, as we rolled paint on the walls. Then I heard the first notes of Elton John's song 'Tiny Dancer' begin to play."

"Tiny had passed away?" Bonnie asked in a whisper.

"Yes, I knew she had, but I called the office just to check. I will never hear that song again without picturing Tiny. It's just like the lyrics say, she's always with me."

"She knew. She knew when she was going and where. She saw heaven," Bonnie said. "Do you think something like that will happen to me?"

"If it does I hope you'll tell me. Now, why don't you call the in-laws? I'm looking forward to meeting them."

CHAPTER 16

I sailed down the hallway as if propelled by coffee flavored with rocket fuel. I had a to-do list in my head three days long and one day to do it in. This morning it was traffic that had put me an hour behind seeing my first patient and I had been running late since then. I accelerated my already frenzied pace as I passed each of my patients' doors. I couldn't stop for a casual visit today. If you weren't on my schedule, there could be no chatting. This was problematic when visiting patients in facilities. On the positive side, there was a staff to take care of the patients and follow orders when I couldn't be there. Also, it was much more productive to see several patients in one location than to spend time with my windshield, traveling place to place. However, I had long ago realized that any time I saved in driving was spent in informal visits when I was spotted in the building.

As I hurried past Camellia's door, she called out, "Is that you? Get in here. We need to talk."

It's the stupid white lab coat again. It gives me away every time. I'm not required to wear one, but I can't figure out a better way to clip on my photo ID and carry my cell phone, pager, thermometer, tape measure, ink pen, bandage scissors, and car keys. Besides, while all of my jobs in recent memory have had a dress code of business casual, one also required a lab coat. I was told it gave a more professional appearance and increased my recognition. That appealed to my sense of professionalism that was created in nursing school when I wore white stockings and a starched white dress from the Florence Nightingale Uniform Company of Atlanta, Georgia. I have always been deeply grateful that the blue cape was optional by the modern time I went to school.

I froze in my tracks just past Camellia's door and line of sight. I could pretend I hadn't heard her but there would be hell to pay at our next visit. I could hear her now, "I thought I was your mother? Is that how you treat your mother?"

Also, I knew myself well enough to know I would alternate the rest of the day between guilt and worry. Before I could talk myself out of it, I turned around and stepped inside her door.

"Hi, Camellia. How are you doing today?" I called from my doorway perch.

"Get in here and sit down. We've got to talk." When she was angry her voice sounded remarkably like an NFL coach talking to a quarterback who couldn't remember which team to throw the ball to.

I edged farther in the room, not yet willing to commit my backside to her guest chair and my next hour to her complaints. I loved Camellia for her spirited nature. Only that spirit could change faster than the weather. Judging by the sound of her voice there was a severe hailstorm of complaints headed my way. Today her dress was bright pink with flowers, an obvious disguise to lure the unsuspecting closer, because there was nothing bright, cheerful or flowery about her mood.

"Do you know what they did? Do you know what they did?" She wiped her mouth with a tissue. She was spitting angry.

"No, I…"

"Get in here and sit down," she commanded. It was a good thing she had once been the cook for the Cowboys and not their coach. She might have been more than football players could handle when she was fired up.

"Settle down, Camellia, and tell me what's wrong. I have no idea what you're talking about," I said patiently, even though my well-planned schedule for catching up my day had just been sucked out her window. The only way to defuse the situation was to be quiet and listen.

"I knew they didn't tell you! You wouldn't have let them do it."

I was still no more enlightened to the problem, but by pretending to have the time to listen, at least she and I were now on the same side of the field. It was good to know I wasn't on the opposing team. Now I needed to figure out who had done what, preferably in as little time as possible.

"Camellia, what on earth happened?" I had taken my designated seat and leaned toward her.

"They sent a new girl to give me my bath."

It took me a minute to process the horrendous crime that had been committed against my adopted mother and respond with the repulsion called for by this crime. Unable to find anything remotely wrong with having a bath, I carefully fished for further clues.

"Who did they send?"

"I don't know, some girl who had never seen a colostomy before and didn't know what the hell she was doing. Where's Musty? I want her back!"

Misty, not an odor, is Camellia's home health aide. However, since Misty inadvertently pronounces Camellia as Cameo, she simply returns the favor.

"She was sick today. You know her kids have been sick all

week. She must have caught whatever they have," I answered calmly. "So the girl they sent didn't know what she was doing?"

"Naw, well I guess she did alright. I don't know why Musty wasn't here. Just laziness if you ask me. She didn't want to come back today because I made her help me clean out my closet yesterday. I needed to look for that shawl my son brought me from Spain. I think one of the gals around here stole it."

"Camellia, we'll find your shawl. That has nothing to with Misty not working today."

"She's going to get a piece of my mind when she gets back here, leaving me like that!"

I think about depending on other people for everything. At this point in my life, when I am so depended upon by others, I find I can scarcely imagine it. Camellia, who once cooked magnificent meals for her family and the Dallas Cowboys, would now likely set herself on fire if she tried to boil water. No one expects blindness or any of the infirmities of old age. They simply show up as unexpected and unwanted guests.

"So if Misty can't come for some reason, who would you like to have help you?" I had to redirect Camellia's anger. I owed it to Misty.

"They could have sent Robin. I like her. She always rubs lotion on my back, just not as good as Musty."

I was making progress, and in under thirty minutes. "Why don't I call Carol and tell her so this doesn't happen again?"

When adults lose control of their lives they usually respond like children who have no control either. That shouldn't surprise the caregivers, yet it always does. Giving Camellia control over her bath was a victory for her, not a Super Bowl, but maybe a playoff win.

"That's a good idea! You call her and tell her I am too old to be showing my big white naked ninety-two-year-old rear end to any more strangers."

I had Carol on speed dial and she answered on the first ring.

"Hi, Carol. It's Linda. I'm sitting here with Camellia, and…"

"She's not on your schedule today."

"Tell me about it. Camellia said to tell you she wants you to send Robin from now on if Misty can't come to give her a bath, because she says she 'is too old to be showing her naked rear end…'"

"Big, white, naked, ninety-two-year-old rear end," Camellia interrupted, smiling for the first time this morning.

"Excuse me, Carol. She is too old to be showing her big white naked ninety-two-year-old rear end to any more strangers. Did you get that?"

Carol was laughing so hard I barely heard her answer. "Yeah. I got that. Tell Camellia she's old enough to decide who sees her bare ass."

"Hey Camellia, Carol says you can pick and choose who sees your bare ass."

"That's more like it." With a smile on her face she leaned back in her recliner. Maybe it was a Super Bowl after all.

"I love you, but I've got to get going now," I said glancing at my watch to assess the damages.

"You ain't going to look for my shawl? It don't matter. You won't find it anyway. One of the girls around here stole it. Musty might have taken it."

"I'll take a look," I heard myself saying, although it was at the moment the last thing I needed to be doing. Because of her blindness, any possession that was not in its usual location qualified as stolen. Probably a few things had been taken from her over the years. That would be part of living in a building open to the public. I was even accused of stealing from a wealthy older patient on several occasions. Each time I was sent to draw her blood, she would hear the tubes rattle as I packed them in the box for shipment. She interpreted the rattle to be some of her knick-knacks. That's just what I need at my house, more dust catchers.

Opening Camellia's closet door was like opening a box of sixty-four crayons. She had dresses in every color, each with additional colors in some pattern or design on them. "It's white, right?" I asked as I attempted to push the dresses apart, which were packed in as tightly as a full box of crayons.

"It's white, and I had just got it back from the dry cleaners."

"That helps." I narrowed my search to the tops of the hangers, looking for a telltale plastic cleaning bag. Not seeing anything except colored cotton, I bent down and looked from the bottom. Victory came in the form of clear plastic hanging lower than her dresses. Pushing the dresses apart, the hanger and shawl were revealed.

"Here it is, Camellia. It had slipped off the rod. The hanger was caught on the pocket of one of your other dresses."

"That's it," was all she said. The only thing stolen from Camellia was her eyesight.

Back in the hall, I took a deep breath. I find myself taking a lot of those in a day. I think back to the Lamaze breathing I learned for childbirth. Who knew I would need it for children other than my own?

With my lungs and patience sufficiently exercised, I headed back down the hall to my original destination. A framed sign to the right of the door announced this was the entrance to the home of John and Bessie McCoy. Each door had an eight by ten black frame with a computer printed name sheet inside, decorated with a variety of colored borders. John and Bessie also had a personalized spring wreath on their door, yellow forsythia sprouting from a twist of grapevine. This was no doubt the work of their daughter Kate whom I had met the other day. At a facility, it always makes me a bit sad to see either an undecorated door or one with a Christmas wreath loitering on it in the spring or summer. It's a little thing with big indications for what's going on behind that door.

As I entered the room, Kate was on one side of the hospital bed and Bessie on the other with John and his big smile in the middle.

"Linda! Come on in!" Kate called out, abandoning her sentry post next to her father. Putting her arm around my shoulder, like I was either her new best friend or possibly a long lost sister, she guided me toward her parents.

"Mom and Dad, this is Linda, the *new* hospice nurse," she said with such emphasis on new it sounded like a synonym for wondrous.

"It's nice to meet you," I said reaching out for a handshake but quickly being enveloped in a hug, first from Bessie then from John.

"We didn't know there were so many hospice companies out there," Bessie began. "I feel foolish now for signing John up with that other one. I don't think they even have a nurse in this county."

"Don't feel foolish. Most people don't understand hospice is like a hospital. You can go to many different hospitals. Some are good, while some are not so good. Hospice is the same."

"We're with a good one this time," Kate announced. "This time I asked around and everyone said we should have signed on with you in the first place. You won't send Dad to the hospital, will you?"

"John," I said, "I heard you were having problems the other day and the hospice nurse sent you to the hospital because they didn't have a nurse to send to check on you. That won't happen again."

"She'll come if you need her," Bessie added, patting her husband's hand.

"I'll come if I can, but we have nurses who work evenings, nights, and weekends. So, if it's an odd time, like three in the morning, expect someone else. The point is there will be someone to send."

"That's fine by me. The only thing I really heard was no hospital and that's what I want. I just want to stay home."

The space was one large room divided by clever furniture placement. There was a living area with a couch and coffee table, with the television on top of a dresser between the living and bedroom sections. Bessie had a twin bed up against one wall. I also noticed an impression in the carpet where a larger bed had recently been. The colors were dated, mauve upholstery on the couch flashbacked to the eighties. The twin-size spreads on Bessie and John's beds matched and judging by their neutral colors were a recent purchase by Kate. Beneath the standard issue floral wallpaper border at the ceiling, the family photographs started. Some I could already recognize.

There was Kate as a baby, then as a graduate, and as a bride. Others were of John and Bessie, aging before my eyes from young sweethearts to silver haired partners in a golden frame, proclaiming their fiftieth wedding anniversary. There were more photos of John and Bessie, with Kate eventually showing up in front of a couple of different houses and several cars over the years, each one representing their life together and accomplishments at that time. There were also some older pictures, dated by their sepia tones and unsmiling faces in oval frames.

This wasn't a room in a facility. This *was* home.

"Are those your parents, John, or Bessie's?" I asked nodding at a picture of a seated woman in a long dress with a mustached man standing board straight behind her. His hand rested on her shoulder.

"That's Maw and Paw," he said.

I couldn't help but smile at the names. When photographs are all you have left of someone, memories get tangled in them. When I think about Mama and Daddy they are the people from the few old photos I have of them, which may or may not be how they looked at the time a particular memory takes place. I wondered if it was the same for John. "That's a great picture."

"They were great people," John said simply.

I took John's blood pressure and listened to his heart and

lungs, making marks on the assessment form as I went. Mostly, I listened to John and Bessie. They had had a wonderful, long life together. If there were bad times, they didn't mention them, or even seem to remember them. Maybe that was their secret to happiness, selective memory loss.

John had been to enough doctors' offices in the past few years to be unaware of any poking or prodding I was doing. Unless my stethoscope was in my ears, I kept up with my end of the conversation. We talked about Kate and Kevin and Andrew and Nicole until we were caught up enough with each other's lives to be dear friends. Dying is personal, and they, like so many of my families, wanted more than a superficial, professional relationship. Eventually, all the blocks on the assessment form had enough ink that I could begin packing up. "Do you have any questions before I go?"

"How long?"

That question is always there. Sometimes patients and families have the courage to ask it, sometimes not.

"What did your doctor tell you?"

Kate and Bessie lost their smiles in the same instance. The tears in their eyes told me the answer. John just looked at me, no more expectantly than if he had asked what the weather forecast was.

"He didn't really say. He hemmed and hawed and said I could get on hospice. That's about all he said. Unless he told

Bessie or Kate something he didn't tell me."

"No, he didn't say," Bessie managed just above a whisper.

"Doctors and chickens often have the same level of courage. John, you aren't walking and you've lost your appetite. Those are pretty big signs. At this point, you may know more about when than anyone else."

"What do you mean?"

"Patients seem to know, and seem to have a degree of control over when they actually let go. Many patients start seeing people who have already died. The end of life is not black and white. It's a shade of gray. Most people don't die suddenly, in wrecks or from heart attacks, but from illnesses like you have. As the end draws closer, they visit back and forth with loved ones here and loved ones there. As you lose consciousness, you are more there than here until you eventually decide to leave the worn out body behind."

"So I'll see Maw and Paw."

For the first time today, John looked like he was holding something back. "You aren't crazy or imagining things when you do see them. If you are comfortable talking about it, please do. Your family knows you are going to heaven. Details are still comforting."

"It just sounds nuts…" he began.

"What sounds nuts? What happened?" Bessie jumped in.

"Maw and Paw were here."

"When?" Kate and Bessie asked in unison.

"They were here the other day when I was so sick and got sent to the hospital." John paused, studying each of us in turn for flickers of doubt. Apparently reassured, he continued. "The strange part is, they were here in the covered wagon."

"Daddy, that's wonderful," Kate said, patting his hand.

"So, what I'm wondering is, what should I do if they come back?"

"Daddy, you should go with them, of course."

"That's what I kinda thought."

Bessie settled from her perch on John's hospital bed into the bed with him. She stretched her legs out next to his and rested her head on his shoulder. She had snuggled with him countless times in the last sixty plus years. Now, it was bittersweet.

Kate walked me out into the hall. Again, I had the feeling of leaving a loving home, not walking out of a room. "He answered his own question, didn't he?"

"Yes, I think he did. I can't predict the future, but it will most likely be sooner rather than later. I'm going to ask the chaplain to visit. I think you will all enjoy Tom."

CHAPTER 17

L et's get started," Carol proclaimed, red hair bobbing as she rushed into the conference room. "We can catch Dr. Kazi up when he gets here. Tom, go ahead and start bereavement."

"The only death we had this week was Linda's new patient at the Ranch, John McCoy," Tom began. He was sitting across the table from me, looking down at the paperwork in front of him. Tom looked freshly starched and pressed as usual. Wrinkles didn't stick to him like they did to me after sitting in a car for the two hour commute. "Linda, thank you for calling when you did. I'm honored to have met him. Such a delightful family."

"They were really sweet, and selfishly, I wish he would have been my patient longer," I added.

"Wait, didn't I just hear his admission report in voice mail, maybe yesterday?" Angela asked.

"Yeah, that's the one," Carol chimed in.

"I spoke with his daughter Kate this morning," Tom continued. "The family has asked that Linda and I both attend the funeral, and sit with the family. She also talked about his death. He went very peacefully, and except for the request regarding the funeral, I believe their bereavement needs will be very low. However, I have to mention something strange about his actual death..."

"Don't tell me," I interrupted, "there was a covered wagon."

"Yes!" Tom said. "The Ranch had called the hospice office for a night nurse when they realized he was declining rather suddenly. They also called Kate, the daughter. Since Kate lives near the Ranch, she arrived first. When she got there, John told her his Maw and Paw had come back for him in the covered wagon."

"So how did you know about the covered wagon?" Angela asked, turning to me.

"It was a guess. We talked about it during his admission yesterday. He had already seen his parents once, in the covered wagon."

"And he just volunteered that information?" Carol asked.

"Sort of, with some encouragement. I'm still not sure why they want us to go to the funeral or sit with the family."

"Yes, that was quite a surprise," Tom said.

"You two are surprised, but no one else is," Carol smiled. I glanced at Tom who was now blushing a lovely shade of pink.

"Let's keep going," Carol hurried on. "Who wants to report first?"

"I will," I volunteered. "I don't think I need any orders from Dr. Kazi, so I can go first."

"I'm here, I'm here," Dr. Kazi said in a rush as he flew into the room. "Sorry I'm late. Did I miss anything?"

"We only did bereavement. Tom and Linda had a patient die during the night. In a covered wagon," Carol said.

"Sorry I missed that! Maybe I should try to get here earlier on Wednesdays."

"Actually, he died at the Ranch. His parents just came for him in their covered wagon," I clarified, at least sort of. "My first patient to report on today is Faye at the Ranch. She still spends her days quietly in her chair, surrounded by pillows. She's usually surrounded by staff as well. Faye seems to be a favorite of the Ranch staff. No change in her plan of care."

"She looks good," Tricia added. "I just sit and hold her hand when we visit. She doesn't say anything, but she seems happy."

I smiled at the thought of Tricia and Faye holding hands and continued. "Camellia. Sometimes I get so... Never mind. No change in her plan of care."

"Misty called this morning after she gave Camellia her bath and said Camellia gave her an earful about being off sick yesterday, then hugged her half to death," Carol interjected.

"That's our girl," I sighed, thinking about how spitting mad she was yesterday. "Bonnie is next. She is definitely declining."

"Yes, yes, you called about her last week," Dr. Kazi said, looking up from a pile of orders he was signing. "How is her pain?"

"Controlled for now, but I think that could change."

"Go up another fifteen milligrams on her long-acting morphine if you need to this week."

"Thanks," I said, scribbling a note in the margin of my schedule by Bonnie's name.

"Next is Jack. He has edema, but as long as he can drive, he's a happy guy."

Efficiently flipping pages in my blue binder I quickly gave report, or at least my version of it, on all sixteen patients. Next, I finished signing my medication sheets and pushed the pile to Angela, nodding for her to pass them down to Carol. Marilyn was reporting now on apparently the fifteen or sixteen sickest people in the world. Instead of talking about the patients and their needs, she was focusing on her favorite subject: Marilyn.

"And Carol, it was late, and I was so tired and so hungry…" she whined.

Dr. Kazi was now whispering into his cell phone while

Carol looked ready to murder an innocent number two pencil. She was frowning, with the hapless yellow pencil clutched in both hands, thumbs ready to snap it, no doubt in lieu of Marilyn's neck.

"Marilyn gets on my last nerve," Angela whispered to me.

"You know she's going to ask us to help her today," I whispered back.

"You're right, we better decide now what visits we're going to make today and get out of here fast."

"Angela, Linda, which patients are you all seeing today?" Carol asked at that moment.

Angela and I looked up and saw Carol holding the team schedule in her hand. Marilyn was clutching a tissue, dabbing at her eyes, apparently having concluded her report.

"I have a busy day. If I could I'd help Marilyn with some of her patients, but I must get to the Ranch right away," I lied. Gathering my supplies, I handed Carol a piece of notebook paper. "These are all the Ranch patients who need visits today." Rushing from the room with Angela right behind me, I left Carol holding a piece of paper that said, "Bereavement visit to Mrs. Crawford" with a smiley face drawn beneath it. Carol was chuckling behind us.

My rushing around yesterday had paid off. I had made enough visits that I felt comfortable blowing the afternoon. Technically, making a bereavement visit to Mrs. Crawford was work. Since I enjoyed her company so much it felt more like a guilty pleasure. I had never ditched work to spend the afternoon at the movies or shopping yet this promised to be just as relaxing.

Pulling up to the white brick house, I saw the flower beds were freshly weeded and mulched. The manicured yard belied the fact there was a very elderly homeowner inside. The only clue was the ramp to the front porch, installed when Henry Crawford was still alive and unable to navigate the few steps.

"Come give me a hug," Mrs. Crawford said, holding the metal storm door with one hand and reaching toward me with the other. Her smile was brighter than the green and yellow pantsuit she was wearing. She had gray curls that framed her face like a halo and gold wire rimmed glasses that couldn't hide a trace of mischief in her eyes. "I was so glad you called. You must have known how much I've been missing you!"

"I think about you all the time," I said, hugging her and then kissing her cheek. "If I visited every time I thought about you, I'd have to move in."

"Why, that'd be fine and dandy by me," she said as we walked into the comfortable living room I knew so well. "Say, how'd I rate a visit on a Wednesday? Isn't this the day you have that meeting in Dallas?"

"Don't ask," I said smiling. "Actually, I've been wanting to stop by, and it's more convenient to see you when I'm leaving the office. Most of my patients lately have been north of your area."

I sat in what had been my usual seat on the floral print couch as she took a seat in her recliner. At the same time we glanced at an empty recliner separated from hers by only a well-polished pecan end table.

"Lord, I miss Henry," she said, giving words to our thoughts.

"Me too," I said. "I can't imagine what it must be like for you. You were married almost sixty years, weren't you?"

"Nope, it was sixty-one."

I tried to imagine sixty-one years of marriage, but couldn't. It would be like holding Andrew as a newborn and trying to imagine him as he looks now in college. There are places the mind just can't go.

"Sixty-one years of marriage and yet we know for a fact Henry would have married you all over again," I said.

"That man," Mrs. Crawford laughed. "He was something else. Do you have any patients now like Henry with both cancer and Alzheimer's disease?"

"No, I don't. Your Henry was one of a kind as far as I'm concerned."

"Every morning the last couple of months was the same. He'd look at me as soon as he woke up and ask, 'Who are you?'"

"I remember that," I said. "You were always fussing over his lunch during my visits, mumbling about doing his laundry and cooking his meals for six decades and now he didn't even know you."

"It was frustrating. He didn't have a clue who I was in the morning."

"Yet every night," I chimed in, "he proposed."

"That was Henry, still thinking he could make moves at his age," she giggled.

"Maybe. I still think it's the sweetest thing I've ever heard. He fell in love with you all over again every day."

"Yeah, at night I'd get him dressed in his pajamas and put my nightgown on, then he'd say it just wasn't right for us to share a bed. After that, he would propose," she said, still smiling.

"I'm surprised, Mrs. Crawford, that you've handled his death so well. I think if I were in your shoes, I'd be crying all the time," I admitted. Losing Kevin now was not something I could handle. Losing him after sixty-one years was even more unimaginable.

"Hmm," she said, "I'm not sure if I should tell you this. I wouldn't want you to think I needed to be placed in a nursing home somewhere."

"What did you do before I arrived today?" I asked.

"I weeded a bit of the landscape, met a friend for coffee, and stopped at the store. Why do you ask?"

"Who drove you?" I asked.

"Me, myself, and I. What does that have to do with anything?" Mrs. Crawford replied with some indignation as she sat up taller in her chair.

"Anyone who can do what you do on a daily basis only needs to go to a nursing home as a visitor or maybe an employee," I said smiling. "Nothing you can say would persuade me to have you *placed* as you called it."

"I trust you, I do. I haven't told our boys this because I'm not sure they would understand. We were talking just now about how Henry used to propose at bedtime, and that made me think of telling you. You see, at night when I put on my nightgown and get ready for bed, an indentation shows up in the bed just where Henry used to sit. I don't see him or hear anything. I just see a rounded dip in the covers on his side near the foot of the bed. Henry died. I know that, but he's still with me."

CHAPTER 18

November 1972

I crawl into bed at night with Mama. The house is quiet with just the two of us there. Nina is living with Uncle Karl and Aunt Muriel now. Whatever aunts or neighbors came to help for the day are gone. I sleep on Daddy's side of the bed. That doesn't bother me even though it is the spot where he died, where I found him. He was my daddy. I am not afraid of him.

I do have other fears. The washer and dryer are down in the basement so I often have to go down there at night. I am afraid of the unfinished basement. The piles of junk sitting around, illuminated by a bare bulb, cast eerie shadows on the concrete walls. Thoughts of ghosts cross my mind as I take the steps one by one, the old wood creaking and moaning beneath my ninety pounds. Then I think of all the people I didn't know who have died in this house. It is only two besides Daddy, my grandfather and my great uncle who built this house fifty years ago. Two is enough. Grabbing clothes from the dryer, I run upstairs as fast as I can.

Every night I tuck Mama into her side of the bed before I get in. She is thin now, very thin. Even as she wastes away, Mama never mentions how tiny and frail she is becoming. Instead she talks about how I am growing. We know I'm taller than she is even though she is too weak to stand back to back with me in front of the mirror anymore. My height seems to please her.

We stay warm and cozy snuggled together. I don't know how long I will have her, but I can't seem to think ahead. I only worry about now. Is she breathing? What about now? I sleep. I'm very tired. Then I wake myself back up so I can listen for her breathing some more. My nights are like a series of catnaps. Listening through the night for her breathing, I am always ready to pounce if anything should change. Every night is the same.

Mama is forty-six years old. She's the same age Daddy was when he died. That used to seem ancient but suddenly it feels very young, at least to die. The doctors said she had less than six months to live. It has been less than six months. How much less? Will she suffer? What will happen to me? I have only questions, no answers.

Mama and I had a fight a few days ago. I feel bad about it now. It was Halloween. I didn't go to school. I told her I was sick, which I do from time to time at the moment. That part is almost true. I'm sick with worry. I stay home because I think she doesn't have much time left and some days I can't bear to leave her.

This year was to be my last year to trick or treat. Next year I will be thirteen, and that is too old for wearing costumes and getting free candy. I didn't have a costume to wear so I found an old skirt in the attic. I searched through the attic and basement, my least favorite places, for old scarves. With safety pins, I pinned them to the skirt all over until it looked like something a gypsy would wear. I thought it was beautiful. I tried it on a hundred times, always spinning around just to watch the scarves swirl.

Mama didn't let me go trick or treating. She said if I was too sick to go to school, I was too sick to be out after dark just to get candy. How could I say I only stayed home because she is dying? I wasn't really sick, *she was*. The doctor said we could never tell her she was dying, and I didn't. I just felt so angry. My gypsy skirt sat unused, a symbol of my misplaced anger.

Mama can't walk anymore. She is far too weak for that. Someone thought to bring in an old rolling desk chair. My aunts sit her on it and wheel her into the kitchen. It works great, gliding across our linoleum and hard wood floors like the house was office space. Still, Mama keeps getting weaker. I heard Aunt Ruth say that Mama had to be bathed like a baby now. She can't even wash her own private parts.

Every day I wonder if today is the day something will change. I don't need Aunt Ruth or a rolling desk chair to prove Mama is getting sicker all the time. I also take care of her and I know her better than anyone else. Something will happen, and soon. I just don't know what. Will she die in her sleep next to me? Will she die while I'm at school? I don't know if she will have pain or if she will suffer. I think of a million things that could happen. I know absolutely nothing.

Walking home from school, thoughts of Mama danced about me with the icy wind. The Arctic air tugging at my school skirt could be a balmy ocean breeze. It wouldn't make any difference right now. Only Mama mattered. I ran up the steps, across the porch, and swung open the door. Quiet slapped me in the face. I closed the door gently behind me, complying with this strange new silence. I listened harder for the usual hum of voices, punctuated by laughter, but knew somehow I wouldn't hear them. The chime of the mantel clock was the only sound as one of the aunts crept forward from the kitchen.

"Your Mama fell off her rolling chair. She was just too weak to sit up. They took her to the hospital..."

The story about Mama falling off the rolling desk chair has been repeated so often the image has been burned into my mind. It feels like I must have been there rather than at school. I can see her falling to the side, landing on the linoleum floor just outside the bathroom door. Lying there, crying. While she was still crying she asked my Uncle Karl to "Take care of my girls."

Did that mean he and my Aunt Muriel would take care of me? Still more questions, still no answers.

My days had a new pattern, school followed by evenings sitting at the hospital. Mama had sat with every family member and neighbor who ever darkened the door of a hospital. Now, it was only right they should visit her and make sure I got a ride there. My sister still didn't like hospitals. She had moved to Ohio a couple of years ago and seemed to prefer being there to being with Mama anyway.

After visiting hours ended at the hospital I would go back to an empty house. Then Aunt Lucy would come over in an hour or so when it was time for me to go to bed. She had volunteered to come by at night and sleep in the house with me. I moved from Mama and Daddy's bed back to the twin bed and let Aunt Lucy have the double bed. I liked her even though she's very old. I didn't mind that she smelled like talcum powder and always wore bright lipstick. I wondered if I could be good enough and likable enough for Aunt Lucy to come by at night for the next six years until I could turn eighteen. It was the only plan I had.

The evenings sitting at Mama's bedside have had their ups and downs. Sometimes Mama won't eat. Sometimes she is angry. Sometimes she seems confused. The nurses tell me it's just the brain tumor, not Mama. That's only one answer to my thousands of questions but it helps. Tonight was better. Mama was alert and smiling. I fed her and she ate her entire dinner. She even looked more like herself, propped up in bed. Her hair has grown back a little, except gray not dark. It sticks out short and straight like tiny pins all around her horseshoe shaped scar.

I watch her hands a lot, like tonight while I was feeding her dinner. I wonder if in a year or in twenty years I will remember what they looked like? Will I remember the shape of her fingers and nails? How her hand looks when it holds mine? Or will I forget? How much of my mama will I lose? There are already a few things I have forgotten about Daddy, and he has only been gone two years. If I could just have them longer, I would be able to remember so much more.

The routine of having Aunt Lucy spend the night had a comfortable feeling, strongly tainted by the knowledge that it was only temporary. There's a saying about "waiting for the other shoe to drop," and I knew that is what we were all doing.

CHAPTER 19

My age has never been a protected secret. It's just a number, and not a particularly important one. It's not my social security number, driver's license number, or the pin number for my debit card at the bank. It's not worthy of a security clearance. Even if I tried to subtract a few years from reality, I would get caught. The fact that both my children are in college is the first great clue to my age. Then when I tell patients I have been a nurse for more than two decades, while inspiring their confidence, it makes it very difficult to claim to be thirty-something years old.

My weight on the other hand, is a closely guarded secret, at least in my mind. The truth is, most people could look at me or anyone else and approximate both numbers. My weight (shudder) and my age are much more visible than I care to acknowledge. Since my age is generally guessed at a little younger than I am, and my weight is an embarrassment even to myself, I have determined that age can be broadcast and weight should be revealed in only the tiniest of whispers, and then to medical personnel on a need to know basis.

Even though I reserve all my female vanity for lying about my weight, this year is different. This birthday was the big one. I have dreaded this year for the past thirty-four years. My willingness to admit my age is not gone, but now I say the number with solemnity, while mentally acknowledging my own mortality.

I am forty-six years old.

Walking into the Ranch on Thursday, these thoughts, actually fears, that I try so hard to push to the dusty corners of my mind, rushed back. Lloyd the greeter was near the door as usual, already deep in conversation with an elderly couple who had entered the building while I was driving up. Passing the squawking birds and heading down the haphazardly decorated hallway, my focus on that stupid number was uninterrupted.

Ten years ago when I broke my knee with the assistance of our dog Biscuit, the doctor had ordered me to give up tennis. Forever. It was the first time I had to acknowledge what my aching joints told me every morning. I had arthritis. My feet, ankles, and knees complained every morning, but as long as it wasn't mentioned it wasn't true. Besides, how could someone barely over the border from thirty have arthritis? I knew well enough that it was both possible and true. The doctor merely forced my acknowledgement.

Accepting that I had an early onset of arthritis provided further confirmation of my short life expectancy. While there may not be any arthritis fatalities, in my twisted thought process it verified my accelerated decline. Losing the only form of exercise I enjoyed, and facing what could very well be my last decade on earth, brought about a visible change in me. I progressed from merely average to well above average, unfortunately in weight.

Kevin has promised that if I do make it to forty-seven, I can have a big birthday party, the kind normally reserved for fifty. He seems confident he will be throwing a party while remaining sensitive to my paranoia. I, on the other hand, use my limited free time, such as my morning shower, to calculate how old I am in relation to when my parents died. Mama was forty-six and four months. I'll be there soon.

While morbid thoughts of my age and life expectancy normally skulk in the shadows of my mind, they charge flagrantly to the forefront whenever I enter Eleanor's room. Turning the doorknob, I had already steeled myself for their arrival. Disguising my morose thoughts with a pasted-on smile, I called out, "Hi, Eleanor, how are you?"

In front of the window was a small, upholstered chair occupied by an equally tiny person. Eleanor is petite, birdlike, with a crown of white, white hair swirled into a bun. Her nose has crooked just a bit with age and gravity, and perched halfway down it are her wire-rimmed spectacles, as she calls them. At present both her spectacles and attention were focused on an open newspaper held firmly in two gnarled hands. The paper dwarfed her, as though delivered by Gulliver to a Lilliputian. As usual, her legs were crossed, the top cranberry clad pant leg swinging back and forth, fueled by some of her nervous energy. She was wearing a pale pink sweater with cranberry piping at the wrists and collar. She could be dressed for any number of activities, with only the slippers on her feet giving a clue to her housebound existence. Unaware of my presence, she continued staring into the paper, a puzzled frown on her face.

Hearing is her most diminished sense so coming a little closer I knocked again on the closet door, while clearing my throat. "Eleanor?"

"Come in, come in. Oh, I am glad it's you," she added, still frowning at the paper.

"Is something wrong?" I asked.

"Yes, yes indeed, something is wrong." She looked at me now over the top of her glasses to verify that she had my full attention, before proclaiming, "I am confused."

"Confused? You? I find that hard to believe. You think

more clearly than people half your age."

"It shocked me as well, but it's the gospel truth," Eleanor answered solemnly.

"Eleanor, I can't imagine that you have any memory problems or confusion. You are sitting here reading the *Dallas Morning News*. Is that the business section in your hand now?"

"Yes, it is. And I will tell you, I was as surprised as you are that I have this problem. Why, I'm not quite a hundred years old yet, not until May. This is quite disturbing."

As I expected walking down the Ranch hall, before I turned the doorknob to her room, the topic of age and birthdays had reared its ugly head. No matter how the conversation with Eleanor begins, it will eventually travel this path. No subject is safe from the topic. When she asked what I did one weekend, I mentioned attending a church picnic at Erwin Park. Parks and picnics have nothing to do with age and birthdays, I had naively thought. Silly me.

With a smile Eleanor had said, "I remember the Erwins. That is a lovely piece of property they had. I am so glad it is a park now. I remember picnicking there myself. Of course, the Erwins still lived there then. We children would sit on the back of the wagon and spit watermelon seeds until Mother caught us at it and put a stop to such unladylike behavior. It feels like yesterday but it was, I suppose, a very long time ago. That happened when I was a girl, and now I will be a hundred years old this year."

She will soon be one hundred, while I am forty-six. It seems that this year finds both of us at the end of our earthly existence.

She is just so much more enthusiastic about it than I am. My elderly patients generally are. After ninety, the half-birthdays even make a return. Children say proudly, "I am six and a half," which only means the sixth birthday has been passed, not that another full six months has gone by. Half-birthdays after ninety follow the same rule. Although in Eleanor's case, ninety-nine and a half is not acceptable. "Nearly one hundred" is the preferred terminology.

Responding to her current concern, I said, "I still don't follow your train of thought. You are reading the business section of the paper, a section predominantly dealing with the stock market, a section you usually end up explaining to me, and you doubt your mental capacity."

"Exactly. Because today is different, you see. Today there is a word, a verb actually, that I seem to have forgotten completely. This is just the beginning, I tell you! Today I forgot a verb, tomorrow I'll be sitting in this chair wearing adult diapers, drooling, not remembering my own name!"

I bit the insides of my cheeks, trying not to smile. She wasn't worried about just any word. She actually knew specifically which part of speech was the issue. Eleanor had lived ninety-nine years in very good health. She was a hospice patient for the simple reason that her heart, like any pump, was finally wearing out. Yet, a fear of dementia suddenly loomed before her. It seemed such an irrational fear given her advanced age. If she wasn't confused by now, it probably wasn't going to happen. Even if she did lose a bit of her mental acuity, she wouldn't languish in a nursing home for the next ten years.

I, on the other hand, had to face the stark reality of being forty-six. Trying to refocus on her problem, instead of my own, I finally asked, "What is the verb you seem to have forgotten?"

"Google," she said with frustration in her voice. "I read and reread the sentence, but can't for the life of me understand what it means to google someone."

Allowing my repressed smile to spread across my face, I said, "It means to look them up on the computer."

"Is that so? You can look someone up on a computer? Well, of course. I didn't forget a thing! It's a brand new word, a word I had no way of knowing! How interesting. Google, google, google. I must remember that one." Tossing her paper aside in the direction of a basket beside her chair, she smiled. Her teeth had become crooked, much like her aging nose, while her smile still hinted at the girl inside the century old exterior.

"Well, it's a good thing you came along when you did. Now I won't spend the day worrying about having Alzheimer's disease. You see so much of that around here, ladies mostly, in the dining room propped up with pillows, being fed. I suppose most of the ones I see in that sad shape are your patients?"

"It's likely," I answered politely yet vaguely, in my usual vain attempt to protect the identity of one patient from another.

"Just wait until you're my age. You'll see what I'm talking about. I know I can't live on my own anymore, and this is a lovely place. Still, I am surrounded by infirmity. Camellia is blind and walks with a walker, and she is in better shape than most of the people here. Of course," she added, as she patted the cane beside her chair, "I realize how fortunate I am to only need a cane…"

Eleanor had entered one of her monologues. My job at this point was to let her talk herself out, out of the understandable loneliness that was her constant companion. A few nods and interjected monosyllables met her requirements. She didn't really want a two-way conversation when she was in this mode. It was enough to transmit her voice and have it received by someone who could comprehend what she was saying.

With my mask of attentiveness firmly fixed in place, I let my mind wander back to where I was in relation to my parents' life spans. Right after my forty-sixth birthday, I began the calculations and realized for the first time that Daddy had lived longer than Mama. I think because he died when I was ten, and Mama lived until I was twelve, I had always thought of Daddy as having the shorter life. Forty-six years and nine months and forty-six years and four months were the sum totals of their lives. Neither had lived long enough for me to think of them as Mom or Dad.

This fear of being forty-six was both paranoid and justifiable. I knew I could get counseling to work through the fear, but every time someone with psychological training heard that I was an orphan, it sparked a macabre interest. Therapists seem to have the same interest in childhood trauma that I have in medical trauma and rare diseases.

My childhood is just a bit too diseased to give someone a closer look. I once picked up a book for adults who as children had lost their mother, or maybe it was their father, I really don't recall. I thought it might be helpful, when instead it confirmed my feelings of being uncommon in the most negative way. At the beginning of the book, it said children who had lost both parents would not be discussed. Survival of such trauma was doubtful and beyond the realm of said self-help book.

So at forty-six, I find myself in my third year of hospice nursing. As Tom our chaplain always says, we minister out of our pain. That is certainly true for me. I am caring for patients the way I wish my mother, my father, and my grandmother had been cared for. Yet, for me, there is more to it than even that. By dealing with other people's mortality, I am trying to come to terms with my own. It may be right around the corner, the one I turned on my last birthday.

"Don't you agree?"

Eleanor was wearing down. She had paused her monologue long enough to invite a response. The inflection in her voice stirred me from my introspection.

"Yes, I mean…"

My "yes" was one I would have given a teacher had I been called on in class, summoned from other daydreams. It was tentative, meant to acknowledge only that I had heard my name called, not that I was cognizant of the discussion. Eleanor accepted it as a complete answer and launched back into her dissertation on life in the assisted living facility.

I am not a gambler. I cried on our honeymoon when we lost eleven dollars in the casino. I went to Las Vegas once and reluctantly played five dollars in the slot machines. Yet, if I were to wager, I would give myself only even odds of surviving this year. Now that I was forty-six, it did seem much younger than I had ever imagined. Of course, unlike my parents, I was suffering from neither heart disease nor cancer. I probably looked a bit better for it.

As Eleanor circled back to her fear of dementia, I wondered if I would live long enough to have that fear. "Very few people seem to leave this world with their mental faculties intact. Don't you agree?"

"Well, I'm not sure," I stammered in response. Eleanor's breathing had become a bit more labored with the exertion caused by her one-sided conversation. She would never admit to becoming breathless just from talking. Instead, she would quite suddenly invite verbal participation.

"Hey, you two! What are you gabbing about today?"

Misty breezed into the room, a black jacket over her left arm, a turbo gulp soft drink in her right hand. Her scrubs today were teal with a darker teal trim. Her naturally dark hair changed color almost as often as her scrubs. Today there were reddish highlights scattered through her short bob. Misty, unlike me, was not overweight. Yet she didn't look like she would blow away in a breeze either. Her muscular frame made patients feel safe and secure, especially when she was lifting them in the shower.

Misty's most notable feature, however, is her smile. She never makes an attempt to hide her emotions, whether she is ranting, crying, or laughing. Pretense just isn't part of her makeup. For that reason, her smile is often just the beginning of a full-blown laugh. Her volume for laughing and talking are inevitably the same: loud. Subtleness, like pretense, is totally absent in her.

"Well, hello there," Eleanor beamed. Her audience had just doubled in size.

"You ready for your bath, missy?" Misty boomed in her normal speaking voice.

"Oh, yes," Eleanor answered, using both hands on the arms of her recliner to pull herself up from the chair.

Eleanor, like Bonnie and Camellia, is an active member of the Misty fan club. Misty gives her patients what she proudly describes as a "good bath and rub down with lotion." This is as opposed to the inadequate bath Misty thought most, if not all, of the other home health aides provide.

"Are you finished with her?" Misty asked as she handed Eleanor her cane.

"Yes, we were just talking."

"Good, because I'm running late, like I said. The only patient I've seen is Opal. Shoot, I almost forgot to tell you. Her daughter is in there with her and was hoping you would stop in. She saw your car in the parking lot. I promised I'd let you know."

"Now be sure the water is warm," Eleanor was saying as Misty directed her to the bathroom. "I'm nearly one hundred years old, you know. I don't want to catch my death of cold before my birthday."

CHAPTER 20

Closing the door to Eleanor's room, I glanced at the door across the hall. Faye occupies the room to Eleanor's left, and across the hall was Camellia. This small part of the Ranch was my own personal Bermuda Triangle. I could get sucked into any part of that space and not be seen or heard from for days. Camellia's door was wide open and the television was blasting so I had no doubt she was home. If I walked past her door and turned the corner I would be at Opal's door. That was, of course, assuming I made it past her door. Not feeling particularly proud of my evasive action, I turned to the right instead. A walk around the entire Ranch could be an hour shorter than a quick hello from Camellia.

I took a short cut through the dining room, then cruised

past a series of oil paintings featuring angels, a few dozen fake potted plants sprouting from mismatched gilded urns, and arrived at the back hallway. Opal's door was closed so I knocked.

"Come in," a pleasant voice called.

I walked into the room, leaving most traces of the Ranch behind. Pretend Renaissance paintings and plastic greenery gave way to family photos. Smiling grandchildren, many sitting in Opal's lap, were the predominant subject of these photographs. Of course, they were interspersed with crayon drawings taped to the walls. "I love you, Booty," was the most common phrase on the drawings, and appeared also on a large poster board collage done for Opal by an older granddaughter. Opal had made the mistake of trying to give her first grandchild the nickname of "Booty," which backfired and stuck to her. Now all the grandchildren and a few in-laws affectionately called her that.

The home-like setting was disturbed by a hospital bed and table, but even the bed had pretty sheets in a lilac flowered print. Nestled in the middle of the field of lilacs was the frail outline of a woman. Only her head and arms were visible. Her skin glowed from the lotion massage she had received.

"Hi, Jenna," I said as Opal's daughter stepped away from her mom's bed to give me a hug. Jenna was wearing jeans and a sweater, and still gave the appearance of just stepping away from a photo shoot, rather than her mother's hospital bed. Her bouncy, shoulder length brown hair belonged in a shampoo commercial, while her perfect smile could be advertising toothpaste. Everyone, except Jenna, seemed aware of her beauty.

"I had the door closed because we get a little loud sometimes," Jenna explained. "I like to play Mom's favorite music when I'm here."

"I'm sure she appreciates that. Oh, hi, Daisy," I said as I noticed the private-duty sitter coming out of Opal's closet. "I didn't see you there."

"Hello, Linda. I was just putting Opal's clean clothes away," she said, her accented words drifting toward me like a breezy calypso song. "Our Miss Opal is looking good today. She ate all of her breakfast this morning."

"I'm glad to hear that," I said sincerely.

Just because Opal was on hospice didn't mean we were ready to let her go just yet. Eating, for Opal, or rather feeding her, is no easy task. Each meal becomes an accomplishment both for Opal and the person feeding her. With her disease of progressive supranuclear palsy, or PSP as it is called, swallowing is her biggest challenge at the moment. Unlike Parkinson's disease, which causes tremors, Opal is frozen still as a statue. Her eyes look slightly upward so it was thought her vision was best if we stood just above eye level. That is where Jenna had been, soothingly stroking her mom's forehead when I came in.

"Misty said you were here, Jenna, and that you wanted to see me."

"That Misty, she had us all laughing while we gave Miss Opal her bath today," Daisy interjected. "She was telling us some foolishness about another patient. She said he was a very important man, but you had some trouble getting him to put a stitch of clothing on when you visited."

My cheeks felt hot, and I knew my blush had confirmed Misty's story. "That's true. Unfortunately, it wasn't the first time something like that happened," I said not wanting to elaborate on that particular flamboyant character. "When I was just out of school, I worked at a small town hospital. Most of the visitors seemed to be elderly ladies coming to visit friends. We had one middle-aged male patient, and he absolutely refused to wear any clothing or even cover himself with a sheet. We took him hospital gowns, pajama bottoms, and extra sheets. No matter what we provided for him he always laid on top of the bed, the door to his room wide open, naked as the day he was born."

"Oh my goodness!" Daisy said. "I wouldn't have wanted to walk past that room!"

"Me either," added Jenna.

"We always knew when a visitor did walk past his door. Inevitably there was a startled, high-pitched scream. We had to do something before he caused one of our elderly lady visitors to have a heart attack. Finally, one of the other nurses said she would take care of Mr. Exposé once and for all. Armed with yet another pair of pajama bottoms she went into his room."

"I thought hospitals only had gowns that tie up the back?" Jenna asked.

"No, we always had a few pairs of drawstring pants just like the gowns, white with a washed out blue diamond print. That was what we really wanted him to wear. We figured if we ever got him into a gown, he would just turn it around, ties in front, still exposed."

"Oh he would! I'm sure of it from what you said," Daisy giggled.

"So this nurse marched down the hall, pajama bottoms in hand. A moment later, she was back at the nurses' station, smiling victoriously."

"Did she really get him to stay dressed?" Jenna asked.

"Yes. We never had another problem with him."

"Why did he get dressed for her?" Daisy asked.

"She had gone into his room, looked him up and down, and said 'If that was all I had, I think I'd cover it up.'"

Daisy and Jenna both howled with laughter, and from what the family had told me about Opal, I thought she was probably having a good laugh herself.

"You must get tired of all this craziness, Opal," I said, rubbing her hand.

"If Mom could still talk," Jenna added, "she might very

well tell a story to make us all blush."

"I know you didn't have Misty send me in to tell naked men stories, or did you?" I asked.

"No, that wasn't the reason, even if Daisy and I needed a laugh. I was just wondering how you thought Mom's swallowing was going? Daisy told me she had some trouble feeding her the other day, and I didn't know if this was the start of a decline or an isolated event," Jenna said, her eyes focused lovingly on Opal.

When Opal had first become my patient, Jenna had asked me if I was an expert on PSP cases. "I've never had one," I readily admitted. "That doesn't mean she won't get the best possible care. I will just have to call our team doctor more often and do some homework."

Since then I had kept that promise and even learned more from helping with other similar cases. My education on the topic quickly brought it to one of my top three diseases I would not want to die from, provided I was given the choice. Oddly, no one officially dies from it. However, losing the ability to swallow has some rather horrific results.

"Daisy is actually the expert here since she feeds Opal almost all of her meals. How is she doing now?" I asked.

Daisy smiled down at Opal, and I thought, not for the first time, how fitting her name was. She brought a fresh touch of spring to patients in her care. Daisy had eyes as bright as her skin was dark. Her lilting voice was soothing in any situation.

It was company policy to refrain from giving referrals to private sitter services. When asked for a sitter, we were directed to either provide a comprehensive list or refer families to the yellow pages, classifieds, or the Internet. The thought process behind this particular bit of policy was that if I referred Family A to Sitter Service B, and something went horribly wrong, our company would get sued. Understanding a policy and obeying it are not always the same thing.

There's no limit to the number of crackpots offering sitter services. There are the criminally minded, always on the lookout for new elderly victims to fleece. Then there are the inherently lazy. Their results could be more criminal than the direct robbers. Leaving a bedbound patient unattended while the purported caregiver sleeps, watches television, or maybe even leaves the building, could result in anything from bedsores to death. Screening these potential sitters is a monumental task. The good sitters appear kind and caring during an interview, but the bad ones do as well. Conning families and patients is their real area of expertise.

So when Jenna explained that the Ranch had become her mother's home and she had no desire to move Opal to a skilled nursing home even though she needed a very high level of care, I told her to call Daisy. Then I told her I would deny giving her the information.

Daisy spent twelve hours a day with Opal, more if she was needed. She fed her all three meals every day, changed her, observed her, and most importantly, loved her. Although Opal required the same physical care as a baby, Daisy stopped short of treating her as an infant. She read to her, discussed events with her, listened to music with her, and provided friendship. Opal was still inside this skeletal statue, a fact Daisy never forgot. At the moment, she was looking at Opal with a frown of concern.

"Well, it is true, that day Jenna is talking about, I had some trouble getting her to eat. They, the people in the kitchen here, always purée her food really well like you told them to do. That day, I think maybe it was not good. You know the taste of the food. There are other times I think she is just tired of how she lives, all this puréed food and being fed by me."

Jenna was standing to her mother's left, with Daisy standing on the right of Opal's bed gently rubbing her arm as she spoke. Both Daisy and Jenna were looking at Opal, but the sparkle of unshed tears was apparent in Jenna's eyes.

"On the days I think she is tired of life, depressed, we talk a little more. I tell her that for some reason that we don't know and can't understand, this is her path in life. I remind her that she is still so loved by all of her family, the ladies that work here at the Ranch, and even you and me and Misty. Sometimes I think she just needs to be reminded of that."

"I have her taking a small dose of medication for depression. Do you think she needs more?" I asked.

"No, no, she doesn't," Daisy answered confidently. "The way she feels those days is normal, then it passes. She is still able to stick her tongue against the spoon when she is full and doesn't want any more to eat. That is the only thing she has now. There is nothing else she can tell me, at least directly."

"We are weighing her like you asked," Jenna added. "She is still losing weight. I'm not sure how much she has left that she can lose."

With that statement a tear slipped down Jenna's cheek and landed on her mother's arm. Jenna and her husband had been weighing Opal every Sunday since I explained the need to monitor her weight. The Ranch was not a nursing home and therefore did not have bed scales. Jenna's husband would scoop Opal into his arms and stand on the scale with her, then subtract his own weight. I calculated Opal's last weight against that of a human skeleton and mentally agreed with Jenna's assessment. There was nothing left.

I thought Daisy was right. Opal seemed to still enjoy life. That comment would sound like lunacy to anyone who didn't know her like we did. There was just something about Opal that lit up when her family, especially the grandkids, visited her. There was a sense of pleasure in her when she was getting a "good bath and rub down with lotion" from Misty. By the same token, when she pushed a spoon away with her tongue, she was either full or mad, or maybe both.

Jenna swiped at her face with the sleeve of her sweater, preventing another tear from splashing on her mother's arm. At first, Jenna, like most hospice family members, had been hesitant to have this type of conversation in front of her mother. It had taken some convincing to make her understand that this was Opal's life and Opal's death we were discussing. Therefore, Opal should be included in what was going on. The unknown is never comforting. Besides, Opal was still an adult, whether she could voice an opinion or not. She had the right to be present when her life was discussed.

"Mom has always been there for me," Jenna whispered. "Always."

Jenna's eyes were still on her mom but her expression had changed. The tears seemed to evaporate and a faint smile crossed her lips as she continued.

"I think I told you both that I lost a daughter. Losing her, well, that's a pain I can't quite put into words. Mom was there for me, of course, even though she was suffering just about as much as me. After all, she had lost a granddaughter."

"That must have been so hard," Daisy said.

"You can't imagine, unless you've gone through it. Mom was at my side as I said. It was just that nothing she said, or my husband did, could make it better. Honestly, no one really had any idea of how to respond to the death of a child. My in-laws gave us a tree, a magnolia, to plant after the funeral in her memory. We were just all grasping for a way to deal with our loss."

Jenna was looking at her mother as she spoke, "Remember, Mom? We had some tough times, didn't we?"

She paused for a moment, then carried on. "So it was the fifth month anniversary of my daughter's death. That sounds strange to someone who hasn't been through it, but at the time I might not know if it was Christmas or Easter, Tuesday or Friday, but I could tell you how long it had been since my angel had passed. That morning I was particularly down. Lots of people told me time would help me heal, but at that point, it just didn't seem possible.

"I asked God for a sign. I knew she was in heaven. I didn't know all the details. I just believed an innocent child had to be somewhere, go somewhere, when she died. She could not be snuffed out like a candle," Jenna said. "It was the dead of winter, which probably wasn't helping my mood either, but I kept praying for some small indication that my baby was okay. Then, I happened to look out at the magnolia tree we had planted and it was in full bloom."

Opal seemed to brighten at Jenna's words. Jenna was holding her mother's hand tightly in her own. "Remember that, Mom? We all saw it. Beautiful, big white blossoms on the tree in the dead of winter. I had my sign. I really and truly had my sign. Then, the next day, Mom, you called me, and told me to go outside and take a picture. I don't know why I hadn't thought of it myself. I grabbed my camera and headed out the door. The blooms were gone and there wasn't a single white petal on the ground. They had just vanished."

Jenna was smiling sweetly at her mother as she spoke, as if she were willing some glimmer of response from Opal.

"Time passed, a few years, and we decided to move. The realtor thought I was daft, and maybe I am, but I told her she had to sell the house without that tree. The tree was moving with us to the new house. We even called in a specialist to move it. I didn't care if every piece of china I owned broke in the move, I just wanted the magnolia to survive. The tree guy said he thought if he moved it carefully, it would be fine. Just as insurance however, he wanted to cut a piece of the tree off, a shoot, to start a new tree in case something did go wrong. That way we would always have at least part of the original."

"That makes sense," I said.

"As much sense as you can make out of something like this," Jenna agreed. "Time had passed, as I said, and the whole story had been repeated and retold so much it was starting to sound like a family legend. Still, I had asked for a sign, and that magnolia tree was going with me."

"Did it survive the move?" Daisy asked.

"Yes, it did. Remember what happened, Mom? This is actually the best part. The tree and its baby tree were both carefully planted in the new yard. Then on Father's Day, the baby tree had one single, large blossom."

"Amazing," I said.

"Miraculous," Daisy corrected.

"Yes, and somehow, I seem to be thinking about it, remembering it more often now. I'll bet you do the same, Mom," Jenna said, still holding tight to her mother's hand. "It gives me comfort again now with Mom being sick. Although, don't think for a minute, Mom, I'm ready to lose you yet, because I'm not."

I laid my hand on Jenna's shoulder. "So I think we need to make sure Opal enjoys her meals as much as possible. That will be easier if we try to get as many calories as possible in every bite. Daisy, I want you to add either sugar, butter, or jelly to everything you feed Opal. One of those will work in each food. For example, you could add either jelly or sugar to her oatmeal. I'll tell the kitchen to send extra jelly, sugar, and butter with her meals, but the next time you visit, Jenna, you might bring a jar of your mom's favorite flavor of jam."

Improving the nutritional status of a patient may seem counterintuitive to the mission of hospice. However, hospice is not just about dying. It's about comfort and dignity. Patients who no longer feel hungry should not be forced to eat. Forcing food on anyone never turns out well. Opal was not being forced to eat. She was still eating willingly. My job then became to make those meals a pleasure when she had so few pleasures left.

"I like this idea," Daisy said. "If she doesn't eat much, at least every bite will be loaded with calories."

"Exactly. Each bite will have more calories, which will make them delicious, as I know too well," I said patting my own spacious rear end. "She will probably also eat more if it tastes better. Gaining even a couple of pounds would make her more comfortable lying in this bed most of the day. Another factor is that as you age, taste buds tend to fade. The taste for sweets is the most enduring," I added.

"Yes, it is. I have seen that with many of my other patients," Daisy agreed.

"Jelly, butter, and sugar it is!" Jenna said with a smile. "Thanks for coming by, Linda."

"It was good to see you. Just call if you need anything," I said, giving her a quick hug. "I can't imagine what you went through losing your daughter, Jenna, but I do know something about what you are going through now. You are never old enough to lose your mother."

CHAPTER 21

November 1972

Crawling into the twin bed, I reminded myself that tonight was a good night. Mama ate every bite. She smiled. She seemed to feel so much better.

I admired the brightly colored sheets that Mama had put on the twin bed for me when my sister moved to Ohio. My sister was furious that her bed had been given away. Mama firmly told her I had a right to a bed and there were precious few in the house. Now I even had a David Cassidy poster tacked to the wall. Mama's refusal to back down on making the room a shrine to my sister had worked well.

Tonight, David Cassidy didn't have the power to hold my attention. In spite of Mama's empty dinner tray I was worried and I was praying. "God, please let Mama be okay. Please God. Jesus, watch over her. Please take care of Mama."

Tears began streaming down my face. I tried to tell myself again that she had smiled. She had eaten every bite.

It didn't matter, and somehow I knew it.

As my tears turned to sobs I buried my head in my pillow. Still, my prayers continued. I love her so much. Please God, please. She's my mama. You already have Daddy. Don't take her too. I have to be quiet. I can't disturb Aunt Lucy. Please take care of Mama. She ate her dinner tonight. I kept bringing myself back to that thought. Isn't that a good sign?

My pillow was wet. I raised my head, held my breath, and turned it over. Once it started, I was powerless to stop it. The sobs continued, one after another, punctuating each prayer. I know Mama misses Daddy, but she can't die yet. Oh God, what if I forget something about her? Can I remember every detail of her face, her hands, her voice? I swallowed hard, again raising my head from the soggy pillow, gasping for air. Lungs full, I let my head fall back down, burying my face in the wet spot with another sob. Please not yet. Please.

The streaming tears and sobs slowed, then finally stopped. While my anguish was still there, it had moved below the surface. Comfort and peace slowly enveloped me as I received a response to my prayer. It wasn't the answer I was hoping and praying for, but it was an answer.

Mama would die tomorrow.

I didn't hear a voice, but I heard the answer in my heart just as if it had been announced from a loudspeaker. At least I knew. I finally knew what was going to happen and when. And, I would never be alone. I would still have a mother. That didn't make any sense, but it was true. Somehow. My fears seemed to dry up with my tears. Knowing beyond a shadow of a doubt that Mama would die tomorrow actually made it easier. The only other information I had was that I would still have a mother. That part didn't make any sense, but it was a powerful message. There was no room for doubt. Peacefully, I slept.

The next day I sat in the classroom for a little while in the morning and in the undertaker's office in the afternoon. My aunts were with me, but not. They were present in the funeral parlor like wallpaper. Their washed out cotton dresses and murmurs blended into the background. I sat alone on the customer side of the large oak desk, only an empty wooden chair next to me for support. When Daddy had died two years ago, I had sat here, in that other chair, with Mama. Both times, my sister, my adult sister, stayed home. At least it was familiar now, the dark room filled with heavy furniture, the faint smell of flowers and wood polish, and the dull ache inside. I have never eaten Play-Doh but it felt like one or two cans of the stuff were sitting right in the bottom of my stomach.

The undertaker was talking about insurance money. Mama had it and it was up to me to spend it. The fact I had no money of my own and might need a few things like food, clothing, and education were carefully omitted. The remaining balance, or concept of one, was to be contemplated another day.

"What was her favorite flower?" he was asking. His hands were folded on the big wooden desk. He had the most perfect hands for a man, so clean, with buffed nails. Men in my family were more likely to have a trace of engine oil in the creases of their knuckles, or a few calluses, and a broken or bitten nail or two.

"Uh, yellow roses," I heard myself say. It was my voice, but my heart was not present.

"So you could put a spray of yellow roses on the casket…" he was saying. Feeling more than a little sorry for myself, I was thinking it is probably sad that at twelve I can picture exactly what he is talking about.

"Or, for the kind of insurance money your mother has from General Electric, we could blanket the casket with yellow roses." The way he said blanket caught me. It sounded warm and beautiful.

"Let's do the blanket. She would like that."

I wandered around the room with the man, looking at rows of empty caskets. My gait was slow and felt awkward. Growth spurts could be a lot of trouble. My feet and legs always seemed to be different from one day to the next. I had begun to make a conscious effort to not trip over them. My red-eyed aunts were nearby but expressed no opinions. Just like the wallpaper, you would only notice them if they weren't there. Somehow one coffin managed to look better to me than the others and I made a choice.

"Then there's the matter of clothing," the undertaker was droning. "We can provide..."

"No," I said, finding my backbone at last. "No, Mama would want to wear her own clothes. Actually, I want her buried in her favorite dress." That thought had not crossed my mind before, yet now it stuck there with vengeance.

"That will be fine. It is something appropriate for the occasion?"

"Yes, as I said it is her favorite." I tried to give my voice the same inflection he had used with the word "blanket" a moment ago. "It is lime green with a pleated off-white skirt."

"Well, usually dark colors are chosen for the deceased," he said in an effort to redirect me.

"Her green dress?" the aunts chorused in horror. The wallpaper speaks.

"Lime green. The bright green dress," I reviewed firmly.

"You can't..." began the protest on all sides.

"Mama liked bright colors. She said they looked good with her dark hair and dark complexion. She will not spend eternity in some drab, dreary thing just to please someone else. She will wear the lime green dress."

At twelve years of age, my mother's daughter was born.

CHAPTER 22

Don't let me choke to death, please."

"Why Opal, how nice to hear your voice," I said. I had been sleeping until I was awakened by her plea. Like the perfume, she had found her way to me. As the body gets weaker, the spirit truly does get stronger. That was the only explanation I could find.

"Please," she repeated.

"Right, Opal. I promise. That will not happen to you. No matter what I have to do." With the promise made, I was instantly back in a deep, and very normal, sleep.

As the early gray light of morning filtered in through the shades I thought of Opal. It would be terrible to fear choking to death and even more terrible to not be able to voice that fear.

Her weight was stable now. The addition of jelly, butter, and sugar as dietary staples a couple of weeks ago had stopped the number on the scale from spiraling further down. Although we had consistently added more calories to her food, she probably wouldn't be with us much longer. Mentally reworking my schedule in my head, I planned to see her this morning. If she could make the effort to talk to me, the least I could do was return the favor.

I made it all the way to the car before that plan blew up in my face.

"Hello," I said after a quick glance at Caller ID displayed the office number.

"Hi, Linda, you haven't got to your first patient yet, right?"

"Hi, Carol," I responded. This didn't sound like a conversation I was going to enjoy, but caught off guard I just said, "No, not yet. I'm backing out of the garage now."

"Good. Jot down this name and number, I need you to meet this new nurse and take her with you today."

"What? We don't have a new nurse on our team."

"I know. She will be on Team Six, but you and Angela are going to train her."

"What?" I repeated. Carol's words were flying at me far faster than my ability to interpret them.

"You know the nurses on Team Six. You don't want them training her."

"Sure I do."

"No, we just decided at our morning managers' meeting to have you and Angela do it."

Reality slowly dawned and I could picture Carol at the morning meeting. She'd been had, in my opinion. She had been given the opportunity to brag about her nurses, something she would do without much encouragement. Next it would be suggested that her stellar nurses train the new girl. In reality, it was because no one wanted to train new staff. It is necessary, but like in any job, a ton of extra work.

"Angela's off today, right?" Unlike Marilyn, if Angela wanted a long weekend she scheduled it off. She was responsible, as opposed to having that sudden allergic reaction to Monday and Friday work.

"Yeah, she can take her tomorrow. The new girl is Sally. Wait a minute, maybe it was Sarah. Let me find that slip of paper."

"Fine. I'll meet her. I'm headed out to Sunset Ranch this morning. How far do I have to go to pick her up?"

"No, no. You are going to Dallas, not the Ranch. Sally, Suzy, whoever she is, has an admission."

"How can she have an admission? I thought she was brand new?"

"She is. We didn't want another Team Six nurse admitting this patient who would just end up being hers. I told them you and the new girl would do the admission together."

"Carol, they really walked on you this morning. You must have footprints on your face."

"What are you talking about?"

"Listen, I really need to go to the Ranch."

"The Ranch patients were fine this weekend, no after-hours calls, no one on Continuous Care. Why do you need to go there?"

I thought about Opal. Carol would believe me when I told her about our nocturnal conversation. However, what position would that put Carol in? I couldn't send her back to the other managers saying I couldn't train the new nurse and do the admission because I was talking to mute patients in my sleep again.

"Fine, I'll just call the Ranch and check on my patients there if you promise I can go tomorrow."

"Sure, now here's her phone number…"

The new nurse was competent and pleasant. Would she last a week, a year, ten years? Who could say? There's so much turnover in hospice, I could never predict who would stay and who would go with any accuracy.

The next morning, the new nurse was Angela's problem, not mine. With my head bent to the side to cradle the phone, I began listening to voice mail as I made the coffee.

"This call is for Team Four. Opal J., a patient at Sunset

Ranch, was transported to the inpatient unit last night. At three o'clock this morning Debbie responded to a call from the Ranch. The staff had noticed Opal had labored breathing when they were making their routine rounds. Debbie started her on oxygen, then had her transferred to the inpatient unit because she seemed to need a higher level of care than the assisted living facility could provide…"

"Daisy!" I said, causing Biscuit to walk over to me wagging her big blonde tail.

"Your name is still Biscuit, not Daisy," I said patting her head. "Such a smart and pretty girl." I flipped through the notes on my clipboard with one hand as I petted Biscuit with the other. A more organized person would have Daisy's number programmed into their phone. I'm not yet that person, but I plan to be first chance I get. Finding Daisy's number on the last page, I hung up on my voice mail messages and dialed.

She answered on the first ring.

"Hello, Daisy, it's Linda."

"They took her. They took Opal to the hospice unit. One of the girls at the Ranch just called me."

"I know! I just heard. Are you headed over there?"

"I don't have a way to get there. I don't have a car, and the person who gives me a ride to the Ranch can't drive me to Fort Worth. What am I going to do?"

"Are you dressed and ready to go?"

"Yes, but I just told you. I don't have a way to get there."

"Since you don't work for hospice, I'm not allowed to take you in my car."

"I know…"

"So I will be there in fifteen minutes."

My next call was to the hospice unit. I didn't have their number in my phone either, but had called them enough to have it burned into my brain.

"Hi, this is Linda from Team Four. I'm Opal's nurse. Could I speak to the unit nurse who is caring for her this morning?"

"Speaking. This is Wanda."

"Hi, Wanda. Have breakfast trays been delivered yet?" I was talking faster than Carol, my Southern drawl abandoned with a need for speed.

"We are just passing the trays now."

"Hold Opal's until I get there. She hasn't been fed yet, has she?"

"Oh, you're coming to see her?"

Patients are put into our hospice unit for a variety of reasons. Generally, it replaces Continuous Care at home. Often, it's part of our plan of care. The patient or the family decide that when the time comes, it would be best for the patient to not die at home. Whatever the reason, patient care is transferred to the unit nurse. Technically, Opal wasn't my patient anymore, and it would be unusual for me to volunteer to drive over an hour just to say hello.

"I'm on my way now. Is her daughter there?"

"Yes, Jenna just arrived."

"I'm calling Jenna on her cell phone as soon as we hang up. Just don't give Opal anything to eat or drink until I get there."

"That's fine with me. I'll confess I wasn't looking forward to feeding her breakfast. PSP patients are a challenge to feed, as you know."

"I know, trust me. Feeding Opal is a scary proposition if you haven't done it before. You need someone familiar with her personally if you want to be successful."

No one officially dies of progressive supranuclear palsy. Death is usually from pneumonia. When a person can't swallow well, food and fluids can "go down the wrong way." At least that's how I usually explain dysphagia. The lungs become the unintended receiver, with pneumonia as a result. If Opal swallowed wrong, even once, she could die from pneumonia. That made the prospect of feeding her breakfast more than challenging. It made it frightening and potentially lethal.

I spotted Daisy as soon as I turned on her street. She was pacing back and forth nervously on her sidewalk, waiting.

"You have a beautiful home," I said as she climbed in the car. For once, my front seat was completely clear of nursing and office supplies. I had cleaned it out yesterday so the new nurse could ride with me.

"Thanks, and thanks for picking me up. I called Jenna."

"So did I. They won't feed Opal until we get there. I didn't mention I was bringing you. I figured we would just show up, coincidentally, at the same time."

"That's good. That's good."

The music was missing from Daisy's voice when she spoke. She was clutching her handbag and staring straight ahead. I didn't think her look of fear was related in any way to my driving. She wouldn't relax until she saw Opal. Silently, we drove west.

When my phone began its belly dancing jingle in the cup holder between us, we both glanced in its direction, our thoughts of Opal interrupted.

"Can you look at the Caller ID for me? But don't answer."

Daisy glanced down at the phone. "It says 'office.'"

"That's nice," I said. "Just ignore it."

As soon as the phone stopped ringing, the pager alarmed.

"It says 'office' too."

"So maybe I didn't call my schedule to Carol or even our secretary Liz today. Maybe. I thought this fell under the heading: Do Now and Ask Forgiveness Later."

"So the battery in your phone and pager are both dead?" Daisy asked, a trace of a smile finally crossing her lips.

"Hmm, they could be. Thanks for the idea."

Walking up the ramp to the hospice unit at an undignified

trot, I punched in the code and held the door for Daisy. Zeroing in on the first pair of scrubs I saw, I said, "Opal?"

"Over there," he said with a nod. The unit only has about a dozen beds so a first name was all that was needed.

The doors are wide to allow medical equipment easy passage. That small architectural detail was fortuitous today. It kept Daisy and me from potentially getting stuck in the doorway as we charged into Opal's room together.

"Opal, Jenna," we chorused.

Daisy rushed to Opal's side as I wrapped Jenna in a big hug. "Thanks for coming and bringing Daisy," she said as she wiped tears away. "My phone was off, I forgot to charge it, so I didn't get the message about Mom until this morning. I rushed here and realized I hadn't even thought about Daisy. Did you give her a ride?"

"No comment," I said with a smile. "Don't feel bad about your phone. Mine seems to be dead this morning, also."

I was feeling better just looking at Opal. Her color wasn't great but she looked better than I expected. I suppose the night nurse had been unsure of her condition when she made the decision to send her. Opal was challenging to assess, even for me, and I see her a couple of times each week. If I had been on call and met Opal for the first time, I might have sent her to the unit, especially if I couldn't reach the family.

"How's she eating?" I asked Daisy, who had pulled a chair

up to the bed and gone to work.

"She's thirsty, I think, just not very hungry. She might be tired but I can't tell. I should have a better idea at lunchtime."

Walking to the other side of the bed, I bent down close to Opal and took her hand in mine. "You are a very smart woman," I said. "I hope bringing Daisy today means I kept my promise."

"What promise?" Jenna asked.

"Well, your mother spoke to me," I began, making quotation marks in the air with my fingers.

"She did what?" Jenna asked.

Daisy was sitting at Opal's bedside, staring at me.

"A couple of nights ago, I was sleeping and Opal spoke to me. My first thought was that I had never heard her voice."

"She spoke to you?" Jenna asked.

"Yes, and it was very clear. Somehow I knew it was her. She made me promise I wouldn't let her choke to death."

"Hi, I'm Wanda. You must be Linda." A pretty girl with dark hair and dark eyes had come into the room. She was wearing blue scrubs, a stethoscope around her neck, and a big smile. "I'm so glad you're here. That's quite a drive. I certainly didn't expect you to come until you called. We were all worried about feeding Opal so we are quite relieved."

"Nice to meet you," I said as we shook hands. "But I'm not the one you should be happy to see. Daisy is her private sitter.

She's the one you want."

"Hi, Daisy," Wanda said. "We feed patients all the time, but Opal's case is a bit different. Thanks for being here. We didn't want her to choke."

"Opal didn't want that either," I said. "I'm sure of it."

CHAPTER 23

November 1972

Aunt Lucy did not stay. My sister did not stay either. Nina, my grandmother, who had been living with Uncle Karl and Aunt Muriel, was moved back into the house with me. She had been forgetful for a long time, a condition not improved by the loss of my mother. She couldn't remember how to cook, which she had never been fond of doing anyway. She had ironed all our clothes my entire life but could not be trusted with anything electrical, and certainly not an iron. She generally didn't know what time it was, which resulted in her dressing in the middle of the night, or on more than one occasion making the bed with me still in it. She could not seem to even remember that Mama and Daddy were both dead, and devoted a great deal of time and energy to looking for them, or asking me to do the same.

So on the day following Mama's funeral, I turned the big skeleton key in the front door lock, prayed Nina would not find a way out or hurt herself inside, and headed back to school. My teacher, Mrs. Jones, seemed appalled to find me in my desk, saying I wasn't expected back yet. I just couldn't stay home and wait for the world to become accustomed to my orphan status. It was better to walk to school, my legs freezing in the cold beneath my school uniform, than to sit in a house that had suddenly become both big and empty.

School felt so normal, a feeling I could use right now. It was much better to think about American history and what was happening two hundred years ago than what I was going to fix Nina and myself for supper. There were no scary basements at school that had to be visited just to wash a load of clothes. There was only a one-story cinder block building dressed in pastel colors and sunlight.

After school was another story. All the sunlight I had absorbed during the day was sucked out of me as I once again turned the skeleton key. With sorrow I stepped through the door, looking for Nina. Buddy greeted me with his wagging stub, anxious to be let out. Nina, however, was never sure I had been gone, or who I was, for that matter. As the days passed since Mama's death, it seemed that I was taking Mama's place in her mind. I was sure that by the two-week anniversary of her death, instead of celebrating my thirteenth birthday, Nina would ask me how my day at General Electric had been.

I felt more than alone after school. I felt invisible. When Mama had been sick, there had always been aunts or neighbors in the house. Food had appeared. And no matter how sick Mama was, there was still warmth in the house, the warmth of family and love. Now there was just a void. The phone did not ring. No one stopped by. Family who lived in the neighborhood might have moved to Portugal or been abducted by aliens after the funeral for how completely they vanished. For company, I curled up on my twin bed and watched reruns of *The Waltons*. The big TV family let me imagine the warmth and love that had been drained from my life. They were poor in material possessions, something I could relate to well. Yet they were rich in love, something I could now only pretend to have.

When I heard a knock on the door, it startled me from my imagined home on Walton's Mountain. The initial fright gave way instantly to joy as I raced the few feet from the bedroom to the living room. I was not forgotten after all! Someone had remembered me.

Without hesitation, I swung the door and my arms wide. "Uncle Karl! You came to see us!"

Uncle Karl was standing on the porch, cigarette in hand,

grinning at this enthusiastic welcome. He was wearing his usual plaid flannel shirt, buttons stretched taut across his belly and protruding over dark trousers. He wore large tinted glasses, which seemed a good match for the size of his nose. His hair was so slicked back the teeth of the comb left marks in the grease. When he smiled, which was often, he had a big denture smile having long ago lost all his teeth. He was always ready with that smile or a joke or a few bars of an old song and sometimes all three at the same time.

"So how are you, Snick?" He always called me Snick and my sister Duchess. I'm not sure why he called me Snick, but Duchess was a perfect title for my sister.

"I'm fine. I'm just really glad you stopped by, Uncle Karl! Come sit in the kitchen." I led the short way we all knew so well, just as Mama would have done. We passed through the French doors that led through the "new" second bedroom, and into the kitchen. As though I had been there all my life, I took Mama's seat at the kitchen table and began talking to my guest.

He was forty-six, the same age as Mama. Aunt Muriel cashiered at a convenience store in the evenings and he had time on his hands. He hadn't worked in years because he was disabled. The story told over and over in the family was that he was part plastic inside. He had a surgery to replace something that had ruptured as a result of too much alcohol, and since the surgery he could no longer do manual labor. I always wondered why he couldn't do some other work, sitting down, but never asked. It would have just resulted in a rerun of the plastic story. He had not touched a drop of alcohol since the plastic insertion surgery, which in the eyes of the family more than compensated for any lack of ambition.

My aunts seemed to have forgotten me after the funeral but Uncle Karl was here now. When Mama had fallen from her rolling chair, he had been there, and promised to look after me. He was here now, proof that he was keeping that promise. He was so much better than the aunts anyway. He was fun. It was especially nice to have somebody to talk to who was living in the same year I was. Nina was sweet and she was my grandmother. She just couldn't seem to remember, well, anything.

"How's school going, Snick?"

The floodgates opened and poured forth every detail of my first couple of days back at school, post-funeral. He let me rattle on, asking questions, and listening to my answers until I had talked myself out. "Are you afraid to be here, Snick?" he finally asked, glancing around at the kitchen, reminding us both of all we had lost from these walls.

"No, not really. I don't like the basement much," I whispered.

"It's just a few cobwebs," he laughed. "If you'd like me to stay while you take your bath, I could. I'd even wash your back if you wanted me to."

A small alarm bell rang somewhere inside. I hadn't even let Mama wash my back probably for a couple of years. The last time someone had mentioned such a thing, it had been Uncle Karl. He took me to the pediatrician because Mama was sick and couldn't. He had offered to stay with me while I undressed for the examination. The nurse said that was fine. It might make me more comfortable. I had refused then, as I did now.

"That's okay," he said walking back to the door. "Come give me a kiss good-bye and I'll be on my way. I'll come back just as soon as I can."

Innocently, I stepped forward on tiptoes and puckered my lips toward him. When wet lips met mine and his tongue thrust inside my mouth, I tried to pull away. I turned my head, but no matter how I turned or tried to pull away, his mouth found mine again and again. The taste of cigarettes and spit filled my mouth, gagging me. It seemed like a nasty, dirty ashtray of cigarette butts was being forced into my mouth. Even as I tried to figure out what kind of good-bye kiss this was supposed to be, he had unsnapped and unzipped my jeans.

"What are you doing?!" I cried.

He mumbled something about me being a big girl, having my periods now, and thrust his hand down my pants. I whimpered as he groped me. This was my Uncle Karl. He was the one who was supposed to take care of me. Why was he hurting me?

"No, please don't," I cried. "Stop that!"

I felt his hand groping further, hurting me. "Stop, stop, stop. Please stop," I begged whenever I could pull my mouth away from his.

Tears streamed down my face as I repeated my plea. I couldn't understand what was happening. He was moaning as I cried. What was happening? Why would Uncle Karl hurt me? Mama had asked him to take care of her girls. How could he do this?

Nina stirred herself and came toward the door. "Nina!" I called out to my confused savior. Karl hesitated and I was able to pull away. Zipping my pants, I ran into the other room. The front door slammed shut as I fell across the bed to cleanse myself with tears. Sobs wracked my body. I cried even harder than I had just the other night after visiting Mama at the hospital.

At last my tears slowed to a steady stream, slow enough that I could focus, and I reached beside the bed for my diary. There was no one else to tell. I was so ashamed. Picking up my pen, I began to write. What had just happened? It was so dirty and so frightening. I wrote down everything, holding nothing back. The poison poured forth. I searched for words big enough to hold the pain I was feeling. Suffering and confusion spilled across each page along with the sordid details. Understanding did not come. He was my uncle, my flesh and blood relative.

He was the man my mother had asked to look after her girls. How could a child, or any human being, begin to understand this evil? Somehow I knew, holding it in would only poison me, soiling my soul, just as my body had been soiled. I wrote of this hell until there was nothing left to say and no more tears left to cry.

I didn't know then how many more nights would end with tears splashed across page after page of my diary. My nightmare was only just beginning.

CHAPTER 24

S weetheart?"

"I'm almost ready, honest," I called from the bathroom where I was standing barefoot in front of the mirror putting in my contact lenses, still wearing my bathrobe. White and fuzzy soft, my robe was appropriate attire for the room I was in, not so much for the church where we were headed. Weekend days when I'm not on call I stay dressed, or rather undressed, this way as late as possible. A bottomless cup of coffee, the newspaper, and my robe are all I need for true happiness.

"Take your time," Kevin called back. "Just remember we won't get a seat if we're late."

I briefly considered applying a little makeup, decided most people would only see the back of my head anyway, pulled on jeans and a sweater, stepped into some flats, and headed for the door. He could have told me to hurry up; however, reminding me that I might have to stand throughout the entire Mass was a much more productive approach. After all these years of marriage, Kevin's understanding of me far exceeds my own.

He was in the driveway, pickup truck running, as I pulled the front door closed behind me. Glancing at the digital clock on the dashboard I heaved myself into the passenger seat and asked, "Will we be on time?"

"Maybe, we'll see," he said, backing out of the drive. "I do want to come home right after Mass. I have to travel in the morning, so I don't want to be gone all day."

"Where are you going this time?"

"Just to California for two nights, then I'll be back."

I would pick up Chinese food the first night, and Thai the second night, eat both out of takeout containers, not wash dishes, and work late if I needed to without feeling guilty. Of course, there would be some mindless vegetating in front of the television, watching endless reruns of home improvement shows while sipping wine and/or polishing my nails. Biscuit and Twister would be there for company.

"I'll miss you," was all I said.

"I'll be back before you know it."

I smiled, genuinely glad that he would be back soon. Two nights was enough. I'd be more than ready to reduce my sodium intake and have a conversation with someone without four legs who could answer.

"How does your week look?" he asked, reaching across the center console to hold my hand. "Are you going to be busy?"

"Hmm, I'm not sure. It actually looks fine right now. That, of course, is subject to change."

"Don't be pessimistic."

"I think of it more as realistic, but this could be a fairly good week. No one is desperately ill, so on Monday it might be wise to get some of my more time-consuming visits out of the way."

"I know what that means," Kevin interjected. "A trip to Sunset Ranch."

"Exactly. I'll go see some of my ladies at the Ranch. Besides, I like to do at least one visit there on Monday so I can get an update on weekend events from the staff. If one of my patients has a little cough or isn't eating well, it could turn into something major in a few days."

We headed down the almost empty blacktop road in silence for a few minutes. The terrain has a slight roll to it between McKinney and Allen where we were headed. Most of the trees were still scraggly and bare. An occasional Bradford pear tree had erupted in early white blossoms. The grass was the color of toast, with sparse green weeds beginning to interrupt the monochromatic winter. We passed a trailer park, and I tried unsuccessfully to remember the name of the patient I had there. The daughter had been needlessly apologetic for their impoverished surroundings. She could have also won a prize if they gave such a thing to the caregiver of the year. I could picture her bent over her mother, but had lost her name along the way as my head filled with even more daughters, mothers, and fathers, an extended family far beyond my capacity to remember more than fleeting moments of them.

Squeezing Kevin's hand, I said, "I'm glad you'll only be gone a couple of nights. I miss you when you're gone."

"Uh? Oh, I miss you too. Hotels and airports aren't much fun," he said.

From his response I guessed that he had also been silently planning his work week.

We turned into the parking lot, passing the imposing stone edifice in search of a truck-sized parking space. Kevin maneuvered the pickup effortlessly into a spot not far from the door. It felt like a half-mile walk, but I knew my joints just hadn't loosened up yet. The usher held the massive wooden door open and we entered, our eyes blinking at the adjustment from mid-day sun to stain glass filtered light.

Sunday usually begins with church at noon (okay, coffee then church), which is immediately followed by impending Monday. Often enough, impending Monday begins during the homily, at least if the homily is delivered by one of our foreign born priests who I can't understand. Today as my eyes adjusted to the light, Father I-Can't-Pronounce-His-Name was bowing before the altar. We were on time, barely. Kevin found us a pair of seats near the back and we stepped over a few other parishioners to get to the blank spot in the pew. Picking up the music sheet, I found the opening song. Holding the sheet was just a prop. While I can lip sync fairly well, I can't carry a tune in a bucket.

"Praise to the Lord, the almighty, the king of creation," I mouthed while looking around, mostly at the backs of heads.

I caught sight of a neatly tied, ruby red bow holding back white blonde hair a few pews in front of us. It was Betty, Jack's mother. Seeing Betty removed me from church as effectively as if I had walked back out the double wooden doors. Without intention, my schedule crept back into my mind, bringing along all my patients and families and what I needed to do for them in the coming week. These thoughts of work spread through my brain like a creeping vine until all prayers were choked out. I stood, sat or knelt at all the right moments, my body functioning like the well-trained Catholic that it is. If only my faith matched my actions.

I had recently smelled perfume in our bedroom, the perfume of a woman dying miles away, and yet I couldn't focus on God? Manuel and Mike both had young grandsons who had seen them after they had died. I had a growing collection of experiences that offered proof of life after death. I tell patients constantly that as the body gets weaker, the spirit gets stronger, and I believe that, too. Then, I try to entwine those experiences into Christianity. Dr. Kazi, one of the finest human beings I know, is Muslim. Other friends are Buddhists. Religion gives direction to beliefs and spiritual guidance. It doesn't necessarily provide answers.

Sometimes I just wished I could be a creationist. Then the earth would have been created in a few days, Adam and Eve would be my ancestors, and Noah would have built a large boat. I'm not sure where the dinosaurs fit into the picture but it sounds beautiful and simple. Those harps and halos I told Bonnie not to count on give a golden glimmer to heaven.

Since I can't seem to ignore either science or my own experiences, I just try to believe. I know there is a heaven because I watch patients go there. I also believe in hell, although I believe it is rarely the destination. Concentrating on God as love rather than a being with a beard or even a gender, I try to content myself with the little bit of faith I feel sure of and not dwell on the immenseness of what I can't grasp.

As my mind wandered back to the Mass, I realized we were taking our seats for the homily. Since I had not been able to decipher the Gospel reading today, a well-known story, my chances of understanding more than a single word here and there during the homily were abysmal at best. Still, the fading scent of incense, the cool of the cavernous church, and the steady flicker of candles brought me comfort. The saying "familiarity breeds contempt" is just not always true. It can just as easily breed consolation, solace, and even form the basis of tradition.

My wandering thoughts carried me back to other Sundays, other churches. Kevin's company had expatriated our family to Germany for five years, and although we attended an English-speaking Mass most Sundays, that priest had an accent as well. His German accent was easy in comparison, no doubt because we spoke German, and our ears had grown accustomed to the harsh pronunciation. I thought of Nicole and Andrew sitting between us in the pew, now far away at college. We always arrived early enough then to sit in the front of the church so they would pay more attention. Sitting up front also allowed Kevin an opportunity at those Masses to make our poor cantor laugh. Once he had worn different shoes to church, not similar shoes, but totally different shoes on each foot. I think one was navy and the other was a white tennis shoe. As she was preparing to sing the offertory song, he slid both feet under the railing that separated our front pew from the rest of the church. He caught her eye and pointed down at his feet, eliciting not just a giggle or under the breath chuckle, but a full-blown bend at the waist, tears streaming down both cheeks, hoot.

I leaned against Kevin, smiling at the memory, absorbing

some of his warmth as I realized maybe I should have worn a jacket over my sweater today. It wasn't spring yet, even if some days were deceptively warm. He automatically put his arm around me as I snuggled closer.

Again I tried to follow the words being amplified through the church. I sympathized with Father's struggle to preach to us in a second language. I knew just how challenging German had been, and I only had to talk to neighbors, shopkeepers, and kindergarten teachers. None of them expected words of theological wisdom from me. Unfortunately, my compassion did not improve my ability to understand him in any way.

Perhaps it was the cool weather, or a smell, maybe even the incense, but my thoughts soon drifted back out of this church and to another, older church. As a college student, I went to Mass with my boyfriend, sometimes attending several times a week voluntarily. It might have been a remnant of my childhood, leftover from going to Mass on school days with Nina and Mrs. Foster. The experience had been new for my boyfriend, and not entirely comfortable in the beginning. His family was not of the church going variety any more than mine was the higher education kind of family. In spite of being outside our respective comfort zones, he continued to go to church with me and I continued college.

"Forever and ever" finally reached through my fog of memories, signaling that Mass was ending, although most of what Father had said today had been mere background noise.

Kevin bent down and whispered, "When he said, 'Forever and ever,' it sounded more like, '*Chèvre* and *chèvre*.'"

We both sputtered once or twice, then laughed out loud together picturing little pyramids of goat cheese, or *chèvre*. Apparently it wasn't funny to our fellow parishioners. In our defense, both of us had flaming red cheeks when everyone in our pew turned to stare.

"Go in peace to love and serve the Lord," the deacon added, just as the recessional music began playing.

"Do you want to talk to Betty before we leave?" Kevin asked.

"Sure, I know she spotted us when we went to communion. I don't mind saying hello."

Patient confidentiality can't exist if the patients or their families don't have any interest in it. Church, Super Target, Bill Smith's Café, anywhere in Collin or Dallas County, I could run into families of former patients, and sometimes current ones. Since I am family at least in their hearts, these encounters become a reunion of sorts. We stop and visit, catch up on each other's lives, and Andrew or Nicole or Kevin would be introduced if they happened to be with me. With Betty and a few other patients and families attending our church, Kevin was particularly well acquainted with them.

"Kevin, Linda, it's so good to see you," Betty exclaimed as

we met her at the door of the church.

She settled in between us, taking both Kevin and me by the arm. Her clothing today had a nautical theme. Her navy pantsuit was complemented by a white blouse with just a hint of red pin striping. A small lapel pin shaped like an anchor glittered in what I thought were tiny fake diamonds.

"Bulletin?" the usher asked as we walked past.

"Two please," I said, getting one for Betty. I'm sure we looked like we only required a single church bulletin, arms interlocked like family, a couple accompanied by one of our mothers.

"Jack is doing well," Betty said with a smile. "Actually, I think he's doing too much. He has organized, mostly gotten rid of, everything he moved into my house. Now this week he says he is going to clean out the garage top to bottom."

"I wish I had that much energy," Kevin remarked. "Cleaning our garage is a nightmare."

"I know," Betty said. "It seems like much more work than Jack should be doing, but he insists."

"How is the swelling?" I asked, realizing he had ignored all my comments about gravity and the need to keep those feet elevated.

"Not bad," Betty answered. "Of course, if he gets that pitting edema again, or whatever you called it, he will have no one to blame except himself."

We had arrived at Betty's car and I hugged her good-bye. "I'll check in on Jack Tuesday. Just call the office if you need anything sooner."

"Betty seems like such a sweet woman," Kevin said thoughtfully as we walked back to the truck.

"She is sweet," I said. "She is also a steel magnolia. She has grace and beauty but is tough enough not to break in hurricane force winds. I can't imagine losing a son, and she is losing a second one."

We climbed back into the truck and I realized sadly that my weekend was all but over. In silence, we inched along with the other parishioners toward the parking lot exit. Once we made it to the highway, it was smooth sailing north toward McKinney. Familiar landmarks ticked by as I gazed out the window. I saw the houses and occasional barn go past, but thought about Jack and Bonnie and Camellia. Who should I see first tomorrow? How would Bonnie be next week? I wondered if the scales would show a weight loss when Opal's son-in-law weighed her today.

"Are you okay?" Kevin asked, patting my knee. "You haven't said a word since we got into the truck."

I smiled at him and reached for his hand. "I'm sorry," I said, squeezing his hand in mine. "I couldn't understand Father at all today, so in church I was thinking about the past. Then, when we talked to Betty, I got just as lost in the future, planning my week. What I really need to be doing is enjoying the present with you."

"I agree with that," he said smiling. "Except you don't have to apologize. It was impossible to understand anything today except the part about goat cheese."

"You were so naughty to make me laugh during Mass, just like the time you cracked up the cantor in Germany with your two different shoes."

Kevin laughed. "Good times."

"We have had a lot of those. I was also thinking about college, although I'm not sure why."

"You are having regrets, no doubt. If you'd gone where you wanted you would be a physical therapist instead of a nurse."

"True," I said with a smile, "but the love of my life wasn't at that college. Following you is something I will never regret."

CHAPTER 25

I popped up in bed as if launched by a tightly wound spring. My legs were stretched out in front of me, still under the quilt. My back was rod straight, and if the room was cool, I didn't notice it. The only light was the faint glow of the digital clock on my nightstand, which read two o'clock. My eyes adjusted to the dark room. Nothing was out of place. The shadows of the rockers and the wardrobe were as they should be. What day is it? *Thursday*, I thought to myself as I glanced again around the room.

"What's wrong?" Kevin mumbled. "Why are you sitting up in bed?"

"It was Jack, one of my patients. You know, Betty's son," I answered, glancing over at Kevin, stretched out beside me, rubbing the sleep from his eyes.

I was still sitting up straight in the bed, looking around in the dark room. The alarm clock now read a minute past the hour. Nothing else had changed.

"Huh? You had a dream about Jack?"

"No, it wasn't a dream. Jack just touched my shoulder. It woke me up."

"Jack did what?"

Kevin sounded as confused as I felt. Repeating myself didn't add any clarity to the situation.

"Jack just touched me on the shoulder. He didn't say anything, but it woke me up."

"How do you know it was him?"

"I'm not sure how I know. I'm just positive it was him."

"It's the middle of the night and you need your sleep if you're going to work tomorrow to see Jack or anybody else. He needs to get out of our bedroom," Kevin said as he rolled over and fell asleep again.

Kevin was absolutely right. I'm tired as it is without two a.m. wake-up calls. *Let me get some sleep, Jack* I thought to myself. Just like when I smelled the perfume, I felt peace. Sliding back down under the covers, I closed my eyes. Instead of pondering how or why Jack touched me on the shoulder,

I fell instantly into a deep, dreamless sleep. For once, I didn't wake up until the alarm went off, then I shot up in bed, once again propelled by that invisible spring.

"What's going on now?" Kevin asked, again roused from his own deep slumber.

"Did I tell you Jack was here in the middle of the night?" My mind was racing. Maybe it was a dream, although I already knew it wasn't.

"The guy who touched you on your shoulder? What, is he back?"

"No, he's not back!" I said, grabbing clothes from the closet. "But what was he doing here in the middle of the night?"

"Are you sure it was him? Did you see him?"

"No, I didn't see anything. He just touched my shoulder. I've got to get over there. I usually see him Tuesday afternoons. This week he was too busy cleaning out that stupid garage. Something must really be wrong. He always wants an afternoon visit. That is not happening today! I wonder how fast I can get there?" I asked, pulling on wrinkled slacks and stepping into my shoes.

If Kevin had asked more questions, I couldn't have answered them. I knew it was Jack, but I don't know how I knew. There were no words spoken and I didn't see anything. I had been sound asleep. When Andrew and Nicole were children, they would wake me up sometimes at night. If there was a storm or one of them felt sick or had a bad dream, they would touch me on my shoulder to wake me up. This had been just the same. Except, of course, Jack wasn't one of my children and he lived a dozen or so miles away.

Obeying the speed limit was not part of my plan of action this morning. I raced to Betty's house on the back roads, not sure if I would stop or not should blue lights and sirens chase after me. Pulling into the entry, I honked at the guard to get his attention and pointed to the gates. In place of a friendly smile he received only a wild-eyed glance. The gates swung open in record time. Zipping down the street and around the corner, I barely slowed to pull into the drive.

I yanked the emergency brake and jumped out of the car, taking the flagstone path in a near run. The knuckles of my left hand grazed the heavy wooden door as I grasped the black metal latch in my right hand. The door wasn't locked and swung open. I kicked it closed behind me, calling out, "Betty, Betty, it's me, Linda."

Betty, alerted by my noisy entrance, met me in the front hall. Her eyes were dark, circled with sleeplessness. The serenity she normally emanated had been replaced by stark fear. She could have, should have, called hospice during the night. She didn't think about it probably because I was hospice to her. They had never been visited by anyone else from my company. Jack in his own way had made the call for her.

Betty's face told me of Jack's condition and her grief before she choked out a single word. "Linda, thank God you're here! He looks bad. Something is wrong."

We hurried together down the hall and through the kitchen. Off the kitchen, opposite the family room, was a small separate hall with two doors. The door to the left I supposed led to the garage. Betty took the one to the right, which led to the master bedroom. Jack was sitting on the side of the bed, feet on the floor, leaning forward. His dogs were guarding him from the foot of the bed. They raised their heads in unison, stubby tails beginning to wag as I approached. They would have normally rushed the door barking and skidding on the polished floors when I, or anyone else, arrived. Today, they couldn't be pried away from their master.

"Jack, I've got to move you," I said. Bending over so he could see my face, I picked up his feet to put him in bed. His eyelids blinked, but he didn't appear to focus.

"What's wrong with him?" Betty asked tearfully. "He didn't look well last night, and now this morning he can't even move. He hasn't said a word to me, either."

"It doesn't look good," I said dialing the office number. "Hi Liz, it's Linda. Listen I'm with my patient Jack…"

"Who else are you going to see today? You didn't call in your schedule. I was going to call you but I figured you must be busy," came the efficient response.

"No idea, I mean I may be with Jack all day, but what I really need is a hospital bed."

"You have to see five patients."

"Fine. Put down Jack and then pick four other names. You can put down six or seven names. I really don't care. My only concern is getting that hospital bed delivered. Tell them I need it as soon as they can get here," I said as I hung up.

Jack was currently in a king-size bed in the master bedroom. Betty had no doubt moved herself to a guest room and given this room to Jack when he came to stay. It was thoughtful, but presented a problem in his current condition. He needed side rails to protect him from possibly rolling onto the floor. More importantly, we needed a bed we could raise and lower to provide care. Also, I could put clean sheets on a bed with the patient in it, just not a king-size bed.

I pulled the covers up over Jack, then placed his right arm on top of them. Taking my blood pressure cuff from the case, I wrapped it around his arm. His arm, like the rest of him, had the muscle tone of a rag doll. "Betty, I'm going to check him out and then maybe I can tell you a little more about what is going on. Jack, I'm just checking your blood pressure right now."

Usually when I listened to his heart and lungs or took his vital signs, I was reminded by the results that he was only in his forties. His heartbeat was always strong and regular, his lung sounds clear and deep. Today, however, his arm lay lifeless on the bed as I slowly released the valve on my blood pressure cuff. A normal blood pressure is around 120/80. The first number is the first beat I hear with my stethoscope pressed into the pulse point in the arm just below the cuff. The second number is the last beat I hear. I stared at the round gauge and listened for the sound of the first beat, which would give me the top number of his blood pressure. The so-called normal range came and went in silence. One thirty, one twenty, one ten, one hundred. Nothing. Just silence.

Around eighty, a few faint beats reached my ears and quickly departed, as if too weak to sustain a rhythm. I let the gauge fall to zero and quickly pumped the cuff up again. Even as I tried to deny what I had just heard, those faint beats at eighty returned to confirm my worst fears. I pulled the Velcro fastener of the cuff apart and lifted his arm to remove it. I gave myself a moment to collect my thoughts by slowly and methodically folding the cuff and returning it to its case. I sat it on the foot of the bed with my clipboard and reached again for my rag doll.

Pulling my lab coat sleeve back on my left arm to see my wristwatch, I held his wrist and tried to count his pulse. It was so thready I couldn't get an accurate count, but I forced myself to look at my watch for a good thirty seconds before laying his hand back at his side. Betty was watching me. She stood so close behind me I could almost feel her breath and her prayers on the back of my neck. Any unusual movements or comments would only alarm her. She knew what was happening. Still, there was a glimmer of unspoken hope in her. Because she trusted me, that glimmer would only be extinguished by my confirmation of Jack's condition.

"Jack, I just want to double check your heart rate, so you'll feel my stethoscope on your chest."

Placing it gently over his heart, I looked at my watch again. The beats raced in my ears. Besides the rapid fluttering of his heart, I also heard some crackles in his lungs. With a little luck and a drop or two of Atropine, I should be able to keep Betty from ever hearing a death rattle in her son.

"Betty, while I finish checking him out, would you grab the comfort pack from the refrigerator?"

"Back in a second," she said and left the room.

Tucking the sheet around his chest I said, "Jack, I know you woke me up at two this morning. I don't know how you did it. I'm sorry I didn't come then, but I'm here now, and I'm not leaving you and your mom alone."

Stepping to the foot of the bed, I grabbed the bottom of the sheet and pulled it up to look at his feet. I'd been in a hurry to get him lying down when I arrived, and hadn't checked his feet when I lifted them to the bed. They would either have a purple tint now, or would shortly. I'd rather see them with

Betty out of the room because no matter how collected my demeanor might be, purple was purple. It wasn't a sign that would go unnoticed by his mother. Seeing the dreaded but expected slight purple tinge in his feet and lower legs, I threw the sheet back over him as Betty returned carrying the white plastic box I had requested.

"Comfort pack," she said, handing it to me.

I busied myself breaking the outer seal and finding the bottle I wanted. "Open up, Jack," I said, knowing he couldn't comply. Then pulling his bottom lip open slightly for him, I added, "I'm just giving you a couple of drops of medicine. It will absorb in your mouth. You don't even have to swallow."

Fresh out of non-obvious delays, it was time to face the inevitable. "Betty, we need to talk."

"All right," she said, nodding in the direction of the hallway.

"Betty, it's okay if Jack hears what I have to say. Patients want to hear what is going on as much as families do."

Her back was tense as she steeled herself for what she was about to hear. The tears glistening in her eyes told me in spite of her solid stance she was crumbling on the inside.

"I tell you what, let's go sit in the family room," I said, taking her by the arm. "We can let Jack rest. He looks more comfortable now that he is lying down."

She held firmly onto my arm as we crossed the kitchen and slowly made our way to the couch in the family room. Betty was aging before my eyes. Her shoulders now rounded slightly, her gait had slowed, and her eyes spoke of despair. Her son was dying in her home, and part of her seemed to be dying, too.

"Sit here," I said, guiding her to the corner of the couch.

Like an obedient child, she sat where she was told and folded her hands in her lap. Considering my options for only a split second, I sat on the middle couch cushion and put my arm around her. "Betty, I am so sorry."

A tear ran down her cheek. Before I could find a tissue, she wiped it away with the back of her hand, sniffed once, and turned to face me. "So now?"

"Now we take care of Jack and of you. I called the office and asked for a hospital bed. I need to call Dr. Kazi for orders. Then we will start around-the-clock care. You will have a nurse or an aide with you all the time. We send the nurse at night for thirteen hours and the aide during the day. The nurse is allowed to give medications so you can sleep at night."

"How long?"

I wanted to pretend I didn't understand the question. I wanted to talk about how long the nurse would stay, or how many nights we would provide Continuous Care. Instead, I swallowed hard, and said, "I'm not sure, but Jack probably doesn't have long."

"You said he would die when his liver stopped functioning."

"That's true. He has had such a dramatic change overnight,

my guess is that he will pass away soon."

Betty's eyes met mine, but I couldn't read them. "That's what I thought. I'm going to call his brother."

"That's a good idea."

I placed my calls to Dr. Kazi for orders, to the pharmacy to get the new medications sent, and to the office to schedule Continuous Care. Often, at this point, I would be out the door and on my way to my next patient. Not today. My promise to Jack was binding. I wished I had come here at two a.m. but I couldn't change that now. I was not leaving him and his mother here alone for a moment. He had gone from cleaning the garage out on Tuesday afternoon to the threshold of death on Thursday morning. As much as I didn't want to admit it, he had little chance of being with us on Friday.

In between calls, and sometimes during them, I wandered into the bedroom to check on Jack. He didn't speak or open his eyes, but I knew he was there. *How did you do it?* I wondered. *How did you touch my shoulder last night? I know why you did it. You wanted me here for your mom. You really don't need anything. You don't appear to be suffering or even uncomfortable. That is past. As the body gets weaker, the spirit gets stronger. I say it to patients and families all the time. But how does the spirit get so strong that you can wake me up in the middle of the night, miles from your house?*

Silently, I asked my questions. Anyone who could touch

me on the shoulder from that distance should be able to hear my thoughts, I reasoned. Actually, when patients are dying I find myself often thinking to them rather than speaking to them. If I speak, it's only for the benefit of the family.

The front door slammed and footsteps pounded down the hall. Being in a gated community, rather than the south side of Dallas, made that only mildly unnerving. Looking up, I saw a shorter, heavier, less attractive version of Jack in the doorway. Before I could say hello, he bellowed, "Get those dogs out of here! What are they doing in here?"

Looking down at the two boxers guarding the foot of Jack's bed, there was no wagging of stubby tails that had greeted my arrival. Thankfully, there were no teeth bared. Yet.

"Hi, I'm Linda, Jack's nurse. Those are his dogs, and they stay. They have always been here for him and I'm not putting them out now."

"I'm glad you're here," Betty said, rushing forward to her son with open arms.

"How did this happen? How did he get like this?"

You wouldn't be so surprised if you had kept in touch I thought, but said, "This is what happens with liver failure. Changes can happen rather suddenly."

The hospital bed never had a chance at delivery. Continuous Care didn't start. Those weren't things Jack needed. All he needed was for his mom to not be alone. With Betty wrapped in the arms of her remaining son, I pronounced Jack and called the medical examiner and funeral home.

As I waited for the funeral director to arrive, I washed Jack's face, combed his hair, and put a clean top sheet on the bed. Occasionally I dried a tear or two from my face with the sleeve of my lab coat. It was a blessing I had rushed out the door without putting mascara on this morning. If I had worn it, it would have just made splotchy polka dots all over my sleeve. Settling into a comfortable chair at his bedside, I looked blankly at my paperwork. From the family room, I could hear Betty and her son talking.

When the doorbell rang, I popped up. "I'll be right back," I said to Jack or no one at all.

"I'll get the door, Betty," I called as I passed through the family room and down the hall.

A black Suburban was parked at the curb. It could have been the vehicle of any suburban soccer mom. I knew it wasn't. The man standing before me was wearing a dark suit and an equally dark expression. "Bill Martin, funeral director," he said simply.

"I'm the hospice nurse," I said, holding the door. "Right this way."

As he followed me down the hall and into the family room, I said, "It's the funeral home, Betty. I will help him with Jack. You just wait here."

I led the way to the master bedroom. Bill glanced in the room, then paused. Standing in the small hall between the master bedroom door and another door, he said in a hushed tone, "We have a problem."

"What?" I whispered back.

"I can't bring the gurney in this way. It will never make the turn from the kitchen." Looking past me into the bedroom, he added, "And he's such a big guy the two of us can't possibly carry him out without a gurney."

"What can we do?" I asked, looking at the small hallway and realizing he was right. A gurney would never be able to make the turn.

"Where does this door lead to?" Bill asked, pointing at the door directly across from the master bedroom.

"Let's find out," I said as I opened the door and flipped the light switch.

"This is perfect," Bill said, glancing through the open door. "I can easily wheel him out through the garage."

Thanks for cleaning out the garage this week, Jack. Good job.

CHAPTER 26

November 1975

The car swerves wide to the left directly into oncoming traffic, at least if there had been any, and then pulls just as hard right, slamming to a stop, the passenger side wheels balanced on the edge of the driveway. The neighbor's yard is perilously close to having a large tire track driven into it. Hopping quickly from the passenger seat, books in one arm, shoulder bag slung over the other, I call out, "Thanks, Sue! See you tomorrow!"

Sue's parents put her in this yacht with wheels for her protection. We had enough Detroit steel around us to go into battle and win. Rocketing to and from school with Sue

I worried, not infrequently, about the other people on the road. Sometimes I also worried about nearby pedestrians. I am thankful as I slam the big door shut—thankful to not be riding the bus, and just as thankful that Susan hadn't hit anything or anyone on the way to or from school. Some days I didn't have as much to be thankful for.

My books shift in my arms as I fish in the bottom of my purse for the house key. My paperback driver's education manual slides across the top of the book stack as I unlock the door. The other books in my arms needed some attention this evening but this is the one I was most concerned about. If I miss a day reviewing French verbs, the world probably will not come to an end. If I fail my written driving test tomorrow, that will signal the start of the Apocalypse.

This is a good evening to study. Uncle Karl and Aunt Muriel are both gone, working at the convenience store. Aunt Muriel works full-time evenings until after midnight so she is usually gone. Uncle Karl still "helps out" a couple of nights a week. He gets paid, under the table of course, since he is part plastic and disabled. Most nights, though, Uncle Karl and I are home alone.

I step inside on the orange shag carpet and in just a few steps arrive at my bedroom door. With no one here to stop me, I toss my books and my purse on my bed. That is one item on a long list of potential crimes. Beds are only for sleeping in this household. I am never allowed to sit on the bed, and certainly not allowed to put my books, purse, or even a feather on top of it. There are so many things I'm not allowed to do, it's almost easier just to focus on what I can do. Even that is challenging because the rules often change without notice.

One Friday evening, I had come home to a note. I was to be picked up that evening by my friend and her mother so I could spend the night. The sleepover had obtained prior approval. The note merely said, "Call tomorrow."

First thing on Saturday morning, I called Uncle Karl and Aunt Muriel only to find out, in screeching tones, that I was grounded. Apparently I was supposed to magically know they hadn't meant tomorrow, as in Saturday. I was supposed to intuit from the note that tomorrow in fact was not Saturday. In this alternate universe in which I was living, that was no longer the day that followed Friday. Friday was the actual tomorrow, the day I was supposed to have called. Note to self: change the days of the week to eight, with double Fridays inserted.

The truth was I had not disobeyed them. The word "tomorrow" in the note had been a typo sans typewriter, when they actually meant to write "today." Anyone can make a mistake. I just wasn't sure why I was being punished for their mistake.

My punishment was not to last a week or two. That would be too straightforward, except of course, I no longer knew just how many days were in the week. Instead, I was grounded to stay home from the next major event I wanted to attend. That way, if the next two or three weeks of indeterminate length came and went without an invitation to do something, the grounding would carry forward.

The thought of being here did not warm my heart in any way. If I wanted to be in a happy, fun loving household I needed to be somewhere else.

Fortunately, the grounding came to a swift end. The very next Friday, at least according to my calendar, was every teenager's dream. "There is a huge pep rally this Friday at St. X," my pleading began. St. Xavier was the boys' high school with the cutest boys. "Everyone I know is going. After the pep rally there is even a mixer!"

Mixers are very important social events. They are dances held at one of the boys' high schools in hopes that girls from the area girls' high schools would attend. Without mixers, we would have little or no opportunity to meet anyone of the opposite sex. They are held in the school gym, usually with a band that compensates for good music with loud music.

"I have to go! Please, please," I had begged and pleaded, but to no avail.

Finally, with tears in my eyes, I gave up. I was still grounded for not knowing my days of the week. Blast that double Friday.

Missing a pep rally and a dance that I so desperately wanted to attend was deemed adequate punishment and I was released to go out the very next night. Of course, the events I had missed had not actually taken place at one of the boys' schools. They had occurred only in my imagination. If Uncle Karl and Aunt Muriel could make up a calendar, I could just as easily make up events to put on it.

With the crime of putting books on my bed now committed, I walked to the kitchen. The expected pot of Brussels sprouts was on the stove with a probable pork chop next to it. The shriveled up meat and cold vegetable made me smile. It wasn't appetizing, but at least I didn't have to worry about what I was going to eat for dinner.

I had worried about that, among other things, for months after Mama died. Nina and I had lived together in my childhood home from November until the following summer. My attempts at housekeeping and cooking and Nina care had been feeble at best, but probably on par with my age. I had babysat until all hours, even on school nights, to supplement the grocery money my sister had doled out. It still wasn't enough money. I had realized that if I carefully folded over a brown paper lunch bag, it didn't look empty. Too embarrassed to admit I was hungry, I took a lot of imaginary lunches to school that year.

The doctor and his wife who had enjoyed my babysitting services had offered me a home. The family of a girl I went to school with had done the same. My out-of-state sister had declined both offers. Finally, someone had called Child Protective Services. CPS had placed me with Uncle Karl and a reluctant Aunt Muriel for my protection.

My vocabulary has increased in the intervening years. I now know the word incest, but still have victim and guilt muddled together. For whatever reason, the physical abuse ended when my address changed. Now my pants stay on and my stomach stays reasonably full. Life is improving.

Best of all, tomorrow is my sixteenth birthday. I will be taking my written driver's test after school, and when I pass I will be able to start driving with my permit. My driving is to be strictly limited to formal instruction at school. There will be no practice in the family car for me. That's okay. Being sixteen means I can get a job and buy my own car. Besides, if I didn't steer the Torino into a tree or another car when I was ten I can probably drive just fine at sixteen.

My evenings have a comforting pattern that alternates between talking on the phone and homework. I watch some television, but there is only one set in the house. If I want to watch when Uncle Karl or Aunt Muriel are home, I have to watch their shows. I can only watch so many episodes of *Baretta* or *Barney Miller* and stay awake. I'm not opposed to *The Rockford Files*, however. As private detective shows go, and they go on and on in this house, James Garner is cute and drives a cool car.

This house is more acceptable than the one I grew up in on Birchwood Avenue. Being in high school, I just want to fit in. This house dangles on the edge of not embarrassing. It still doesn't have a single brick. It does have two actual bedrooms instead of a dining room pretending to be a bedroom. My bedroom is tiny, but I really don't care. The two twin beds, nightstand, and small chest of drawers take up almost every inch of floor space. It's a good thing my feet are small or I would probably trip with every step.

When I moved in, I shared the room with Aunt Muriel's youngest daughter from her first marriage. Uncle Karl married Aunt Muriel when she had several young daughters still living at home. Her oldest children had already moved out. I can't blame her for not wanting to take me in after raising so many children. I do have some suspicions about why Uncle Karl decided to marry a woman with daughters at home. True love does not top the list.

When the last child moved into her own apartment, Aunt Muriel let me pick out my own bedspreads and curtains. I chose a pattern with a yellow background and a riot of flowers all over them. I wanted to paint the walls yellow but she wouldn't let me. In the end, she painted the ceiling yellow for me and kept the walls white. It feels warm and sunny all year round. I'm not allowed to put anything on the beds, like books or even myself, unless I'm sleeping. It's hard to have friends over because there is nowhere to sit.

I like to go to my friends' houses instead. It's amazing to see how other people live. Bedrooms and bathrooms are both plural in their houses. Bridget has the prettiest house of all, with red bricks and lots of trees in the yard. My friend Holly has a bedroom at least as big as half of this house, and her very own horse. Teresa is one of seven children and lives in a house big enough for all of them. She and Holly are both getting their own cars. Teresa is getting a hand-me-down car. Holly is getting a Volvo.

I don't envy them for what they have. Mama and Daddy always said that they were going to keep their 1965 Mustang for me. When I turned sixteen, I would get it. Even though everything from my past life was sold, it still counts somehow. They loved me, a fact I remind myself of not infrequently. Someday I will buy a car and eventually I plan to not wait in line to use the bathroom. I will also have some bricks on my house.

Tonight, I just plan to enjoy my solitude and study comfortably. On my bed. Putting my pillow up against the headboard, I stretch out. Dutifully, I place my blue French book on my lap and open it. *"Ce n'est pas possible!"*

Tossing the textbook aside, I decide I would rather face Madame Cheney tomorrow and explain to her in French why

I didn't do my French homework than possibly fail my written driving test. The driving manual is dog-eared and worn. If my textbooks looked this used I could possibly be ranked at the top of my class. That's not going to happen. I love some of my classes, like French, German, and art, just not enough to work myself to death over them. After all, next year is my senior year, my last year before freedom. It's not like I'm going to college or anything. Uncle Karl and Aunt Muriel always talk about how important it is to get a real job and make some money, instead of just wasting more time in school.

"Concentrate," I say out loud to myself, opening the book. The list of restrictions includes vision. I have to take the eye exam tomorrow. I'm willing to bet I can't pass it without my glasses. That's okay. Left turns, right turns, those rules are so obvious. Well, maybe they aren't always obvious to Sue. Yet she passed her test, so I have to be able to do this.

I can't believe I'm going to be sixteen tomorrow. Daddy died when I was ten. Mama died when I was twelve. Nina died when I was fourteen. I should be afraid of even numbered birthdays. I'm not. The pattern is there but it doesn't frighten me. I look forward to sixteen with only anticipation. Besides, there is no one left to lose.

Safe stopping distances, I know them by heart. Road signs. Maybe I should give them another look. They're just so obvious. They have pictures of curves and falling rocks, for heaven's sake.

Still, everyone who has gone before me to take the test tells the same story. There are trick questions everywhere. I must be prepared.

Mama got her license as an adult. When my grandfather, Daddy's father, passed away, Mama inherited his car. She took driving lessons from the Yellow Cab Company and passed her driving test with a score of ninety-five. That was the actual driving portion that I would take a month from now after having some experience behind the wheel. I don't know what she scored on the written test I will be taking tomorrow and I will never be able to ask. So ninety-five will be the standard, trick questions and all.

I stretch again and glance up from the book. She is standing in the doorway, watching me. A feeling of peace washes over me. I wonder how long she has been standing there. She looks beautiful, especially her hair. It is thick and dark, just as I remember, with some curl to it. There is no scar, no shaved head with short, mostly gray stubble growing in.

She looks like my memories of her, only better, if that's possible. She is so beautiful. When she smiles, I notice how her green eyes light up and realize it is like my own eyes looking back at me. Did my aunts see that before? I had never noticed our resemblance. Now it seems obvious. Maybe that had something to do with them avoiding me after the funeral. Suddenly, I feel just a bit more charitable toward them.

"Mama," I say softly.

She is still smiling at me and I feel the warmth of her love envelop me. She is wearing the bright green dress with the off-white pleated skirt. I try to absorb everything about the moment, basking in her love, love I have missed so desperately.

"Why haven't I seen you before?" Even with the love I feel from her and return so readily, the pain of my abandonment is still there. I don't care. I need to know. If she can stand before me now, where was she all the times I have needed her? This miraculous visit is a gift beyond my mortal comprehension, yet the torture I have suffered, alone, is also beyond comprehension.

"I have been with you."

Her words wash over me. I take them in, slowly digesting their meaning. The night before she died, I was told not just that she was going to die the next day, but that I would always have a mother. Understanding dawned. I wouldn't have just any mother. I would have *my* mama. Mama is still with me. She has always, somehow, been with me. I feel joy and peace at her presence, reassurance and comfort with her words. Yet, as I try to grapple with this presence, her ability to stand before me on the eve of my birthday, I circle back to my question. How much easier it would have been if she had revealed this ability to me sooner.

I believe in God and I believe in heaven. However, I thought "passing away" as it is called, was just that. I thought it was a journey that took the departed away, far away. Maybe there are no clouds for pillows. I never really bought into that image. Still, it seemed like there would be a distance of time and space, something out of science fiction. It certainly never occurred to me that she was here.

"You've been with me all along?" I questioned. I thought of the torture I went through after her death. Uncle Karl, or Pop as he was now called, molesting me over and over. I thought of those late nights I spent babysitting trying to earn money so Nina and I could eat. The nights I had gone to bed hungry. The days I didn't want to live. The day I came home from school to the smell of gas because Nina had turned all the knobs on the stove. The day a neighbor beat Buddy our dog because Nina had let him out.

Mama was with me even then. I knew that now. My survival was proof. At twelve years old, I was not ready to lose my mother. Now I knew I would never really lose her. My life still seemed traumatic, but no longer felt like a tragedy. Tragedies have sad endings, an ending I would not accept. I couldn't control what had happened to me so far, but that would not always be the case. Sixteen brought me another step closer to control over my life, independence.

I continued looking at her, trying to absorb her love and presence, burning the moment into my memory. Her hands looked just as I remembered them. I hadn't forgotten anything about her, yet I continued my wide-eyed stare. I didn't want to lose anything of Mama. My memories of Daddy had already faded, merging into the few old black and white pictures I still had of him.

"Will I see you again?"

"You will hear from me again."

"When?" I was already anticipating our next encounter. "When will I hear from you again?"

"I'll be there when you need me."

I need you every minute of every day I thought, but she was gone. The difference now, and forever, would be that she was gone from my sight only.

CHAPTER 27

H on, hon, wake up."
  "Huh?"

"Wake up, your pager is going off."

"Hmm? What? Okay."

Through a dense fog, an annoying, repetitive beep was drilling a hole through my earplugs and into my brain. Abruptly, it was joined in a macabre resonance by the ringing of the phone. Saturday, sleepy, tired.

"Hello? Yes, hang on just a minute. She's right here. Honey, it's the office. You're on call," Kevin said as he gingerly passed the phone to me, afraid the device would light my very short fuse.

"Damn," I said to myself, "Thanks," to Kevin, and "What?"

into the receiver.

"Linda, you're on call today and we have some visits for you to make," stated the matter-of-fact voice on the other end. There was no acknowledgement that my forty hour week had been worked, completed in a mere fifty or sixty hours. No matter how many hours I put in for travel and patient visits, the time I entered counted as eight hours every day. I was salaried. Lucky me. Today would be paid as fee for service however, each visit a little more money, mostly for taxes. Still, no fee could replace much needed sleep, errands, or housework and yard work. Worst of all, doing this job six days in a week took a toll on me that would carry through to the following week. I couldn't recover enough tomorrow to be ready for Monday.

"Hold on, let me get some paper and a pen to write this down," I said with the enthusiasm of a woman preparing to write down the instructions for a do-it-yourself root canal.

My usually precise handwriting was reduced to a scrawl, primarily by anger. As I wrote the sixth patient name and address down, the fuse ignited. "You know I've worked all week! How many visits do you plan to give me?"

"You're on call. You have to make the visits. Six is all we have for you now, but be sure to call back when you're done. Something else may come up. We may also have an admission for you this evening in Rockwall if the patient gets discharged from the hospital," the weekend administrator added with detectable glee in her voice. I thought about asking if this was her retirement job and if she was originally from Kentucky. She may have previously been employed conducting nursing school interviews. I couldn't be sure.

"Oh yes, I will hurry and call back as soon as I'm done," I said, mock enthusiasm dripping from my voice as I hung up the phone. "What I'll really do is take my sweet time and call you back eventually, if you're lucky. It's not like I have the energy to rush." The last part was spoken in the direction of the silent receiver, just to vent some steam.

"How bad is it?" Kevin asked now that he was fully awake. He had rolled toward me, raised up on an elbow, looking sad and sleepy at the same time.

"It's bad, a full day at least. It sounds like they may have plans to work me twelve hours. It will probably take that long anyway. None of the patients are in any of my usual areas and they are pretty spread out. It will take me longer just to find them and then it always takes me longer to talk to the families when I don't know them," I said, sitting up in bed, reluctant to push back the quilt I had pulled over me while writing my patient list. "I hate my job."

"Quit," he said simply, and I knew he meant it.

"I can't. I detest the paperwork, and I despise being on call. As much as I hate my job, that's how much I love my patients."

"I know. There's no solution I can offer when you put it

that way. Do you want me to make coffee while you take a shower?"

"No, I'll make coffee. I'm not in a rush. The faster I go, the more they will pile on. And I really don't have the energy. Sorry they woke you up."

"That's okay. What do you need me to do today while you're working?"

I looked at Kevin and felt homesick even though I was at least an hour from leaving the house. As much as he works and travels during the week, Saturday and Sunday are often our only days together. Going to the hardware store, maybe going out to breakfast, or just having coffee on the front porch sounded like heaven. Working another day, being away from him and our home, sounded like unadulterated hell. Whining more was not going to be productive so all I asked was, "Can you pick up the dry cleaning?"

"Sure, and what about tonight? Do you still want to get together with C.J. and Sandy, or will you be too tired?"

"We're supposed to go to their house. Sandy and I already talked about it. She knew we wouldn't have them over here in case I did get called out today," I sighed, thinking about the day and evening ahead. C.J. and Sandy were our best friends and Saturday night was almost always reserved for dinner at one of our houses. It was the night Sandy and I could cook and actually enjoy it, weekday pressures washed away by a good cabernet. "I know I'll be tired. If I'm not home by six tonight just go on over to their house and I'll join you when I get finished. But don't expect much from me."

Kevin was smiling. I knew he was pleased I didn't want to cancel our evening plans. It just didn't seem fair to ask him to be home alone today, only to spend the evening watching television while I likely completed the rest of my paperwork and then slept in my chair. I reached over and gave him a quick kiss, and threw back the warm covers before I completely changed my mind about starting the day.

In just under an hour I was standing in the kitchen with my purse over my shoulder, map and directions in my hand. I had showered and pulled my hair back into a ponytail that hopefully would hold for a good twelve hours or so. The only thing I ever got in trouble for in nursing school was having my hair free itself slightly from a tight bun and brush the edge of my collar by the end of my hospital shift. That had been a federal offense in those days, leaving me to wonder if I would have been shot on sight if I actually made a medication error or committed some other infraction against a patient. The lesson had not been lost on me, and a quarter of a century later I was still concerned about appearing professional to patients and families, even when it was my sixth day to work, and a twelve hour shift at that.

My one concession to forced overtime was my clothing. No

one was going to make me iron slacks or a skirt on a Saturday. The thought of ironing any day of the week is only slightly more appealing than a full frontal lobotomy. However, our hospice has a strict rule against blue jeans for field staff. Mine were black.

I plopped down into the Volkswagen and looked at my patient list. The seat heater immediately began warming me but did not begin to compare to the warmth of snuggling under a quilt with Kevin. I sighed deeply and tried to choke back my annoyance with life, our office in particular. The patients and families listed on the papers in my hand deserved my best, and I knew from experience being on call usually brought me in contact with people who needed my help the most. Damn.

It didn't really matter what order I saw the patients in today. I would get paid mileage from my house and back again, in accordance with some IRS rule pertaining to after-hours work. After looking over my printed directions and thumbing through my map book, I decided on a route. I debated for a moment on throwing my pager and cell phone out the window and backing over them repeatedly. I considered the one hundred dollar fee for lost or damaged pagers, and opted to put them in the cup holder instead.

My selected first visit of the day promised to be uncomplicated. This was a nursing home patient on Continuous Care. Pulling up to the nursing home I wished finding other patients could be this simple. Brick pillars held an enormous sign in place, proclaiming the name of the home and the street address. I would be lucky the rest of the day if my patients had any house numbers visible from the street.

My black and gray sneakers, which I was technically not wearing, squeaked as I walked down the fluorescent, antiseptic corridor. It amazes me when my beloved Sunset Ranch is referred to as a nursing home instead of an assisted living facility. The gilded halls of the Ranch and its homey atmosphere had nothing in common with the sterile, dull white passageway I was currently traversing.

A woman leaning perceptibly to the right in a wheelchair reached a hand in my direction, her eyes blank, drool at the corner of her mouth. "Hi! It's so good to see you today!" I said, taking her hand. "You have a very pretty pink robe on. I can't stay and visit, but have a good day."

Checking my notes again, I found my patient's room and knocked lightly on the door. It was a double room with no one assigned the bed by the door. The curtain was drawn between the two beds and I peeked around it to find the Continuous Care aide sitting in a straight back chair watching television. The waif-like patient was positioned on her side by pillows larger than she was. "Hi, I'm Linda, the hospice nurse."

"Marcus, I work for a staffing agency. I don't think we've met," the aide said standing to shake my hand.

Little old ladies usually do not like having male nurses or aides take care of them. Little old white ladies scream, not infrequently, if an African American male tries to give them a bath. When they are unable to scream for themselves, the family and friends make this wish known to us. Before me, however, was a very old, very white woman, being cared for by a male aide, the color of the ink in my pen and my jeans before their first wash, who I now knew as Marcus.

"Nice to meet you, Marcus," I said, shaking hands. "So the family is not involved?"

"No one ever visits her. How did you know?"

"Just a hunch," I replied, stepping over to the patient's bedside. "Hello, Pearl, I'm Linda. We haven't met before. I came by to check on you today."

As expected, the only response was from Marcus. "She isn't in any pain. My notes, including her current vital signs are on the bedside table. I was wondering, if you are going to be a few minutes can I run across the street to the pharmacy? I'm diabetic and need to pick up my insulin. When I get off tonight, they'll be closed, and no telling what my blood sugar will be by then…"

Inwardly I sighed again, calculating the time it would take Marcus to go to the pharmacy, leaving me to babysit Pearl. Outwardly I said, "Sure, I'll stay with her. Just try to hurry. I have at least five more people to see."

My last sentence landed on Marcus's back, if it caught him at all. He was out the door. I had serious doubts that Ms. Pink Robe would be able to even graze him with a touch as he ran by. My only hope was that he was in half as big a hurry to return to Pearl.

"Pearl, it's just you and me," I said lightly rubbing her pencil-thin arm. "First, I'm going to listen to your heart and lungs. When I finish checking you out, I will give... hang on a second."

I fumbled through my hastily scrawled notes from this morning and found Pearl's name and address. Underneath I had written "Judy" and a phone number.

"I will give your daughter Judy a call to let her know how her mama is doing. I'm sure she is concerned."

A shadow of a frown crossed Pearl's face as I said "Judy." It wasn't the furrowed brow associated with pain. Instead it was a look of concentration, like she wanted to say something in response. The look passed as quickly as it came, just noticeable enough to cause a twinge of concern.

With her physical assessment finished, I attached a three-page carbon note to my clipboard and settled in Marcus's abandoned chair. As promised, I pulled my cell phone from my pocket and dialed Judy's number, hoping to check off blocks on the form as I updated the unknown daughter on Miss Pearl's condition.

"Hi there! This is Judy, leave a message at the tone," was the instant reply, along with the promised beep.

"Judy, my name is…"

"Mailbox full."

So much for updates or even messages. With my undivided attention on the annoying form, I made quick work of it. I signed it, giving it a final check for accuracy, and noticed my normally neat handwriting had made a return. As I was tearing apart the carbons, my phone began playing the belly dancing song, causing a shiver of panic to run down my spine. *Not the office, please, not the office* I thought as I pulled it from my lab coat pocket. In my panic, I accidentally hit the talk button and a voice began squawking at me before I could get it to my ear.

"Hi, this is Linda," I interrupted. "Who is this?"

"Who are you? You called me."

Recognition dawned. "Oh, hello, Judy. This is Linda. I work for hospice and I am…"

"Did Mother die?"

"No, no. She's fine, well maybe fine is a strong word…"

"I told her regular nurse, Marcie is her name, not to bother me…"

"We don't have a nurse named Marcie," I interjected. Talking over Judy was the only available option for expressing anything other than a dial tone. I knew her kind. If I hung up on her, even accidentally on purpose, she would make the time to call the office and get me in trouble.

"I told her how busy I am with this project at work," Judy continued, ignoring my interruption.

"Stacey! We have a Stacey on the nursing home team!" I exclaimed after mentally trying to find a nurse whose name in some way resembled the phantom Marcie, either by rhyming or starting with the same letter.

"Marcie, Stacey, whoever, knows not to bother me unless it's important. I've got to run, but make sure you people quit bothering me."

"I'll make sure," I said to no one at all. I felt certain the silence at the other end had not resulted from a dropped call, but from a daughter dropped out of her mother's life.

I pulled the carbon back out of Pearl's chart and lining up the original and carbon, carved out in large block letters, "DO NOT CALL JUDY, PER HER REQUEST."

I wouldn't be on call again before Pearl passed away, so at least I wouldn't be the one notifying Judy of that news. Pearl's death would likely cause the festering guilt to bubble to the surface, and boil over onto the innocent messenger in the form of rage. I was much better off just sitting here waiting, hoping for Marcus's return, than dealing with this particular daughter.

Uninterested in reruns of 1960s era Westerns broadcast in black and white on Pearl's television, I turned my attention to her. "Pearl, I just talked to your daughter, Judy."

Hearing and smell always seem to be the last senses to go. With that in mind, I knew Pearl could hear me. What I didn't know was how much of the phone conversation she had heard. The same look of concentration flickered across her face again at the mention of her daughter's name. Pearl was technically in a coma. That didn't mean she had left the building.

"I'll make sure," I told Pearl now, working with the last words I had tried to squeeze into my attempted conversation with Judy. "I'm supposed to make sure I tell you that Judy loves you very much, Pearl. You raised a hard worker. She's working so hard in fact on her big project that she can't be here today. Just know that she loves you very much."

Her wrinkled face had looked ashen but relaxed when I arrived. The white hair curled around it softly. Now, she still looked angelic, but possibly more peaceful. Her cheeks seemed to turn pink, just a bit, at the thought of her daughter's love. What had transpired between Pearl and Judy, I would never know. Quite honestly, I didn't really care. I only wanted Pearl to be peaceful, and Diabetic Marcus to return.

Marcus's eventual return looked like the baton exchange of a relay race in the overweight Olympics. He came in the door, supersized meal in one hand and extra large drink in the other, leaving little room for doubt about the cause of his diabetes. I waddled past, calling behind me, "Pearl is fine. Don't call the daughter."

Mentally, I was moving on to the next patient on my list. Traffic and distance made that problematic, rather than instantaneous. I was behind on my schedule after seeing just one patient, and feeling flustered. There was only one thing I could do while driving that would make me feel better, at least one thing other than stopping for my own supersized meal. I needed to bitch.

"Hi Angela! Are you busy?"

"No, but don't tell me you are working today?"

The intuitive voice on the other end was both sympathetic to my plight and angry on my behalf. Angela was just what the doctor ordered. Sandy would have been sympathetic, and probably grocery shopping for tonight, if I had called her. Her advice would have been the same as Kevin's. Just quit. Angela would at least be acquainted with the sixteen or seventeen reasons I couldn't do that. She had met more than a few of them personally.

"Slaving away is more like it," I replied, bitterness dripping from each word.

"I'm on call tomorrow. That means they will probably use me also. Do you know if someone called in sick this weekend, or is today just a busy day?"

"I was too upset, and sleepy, to ask this morning, but since they gave me a full day's work early this morning, I suppose someone on the weekend staff called in sick. They hadn't had time to get busy yet when they woke me up."

"When someone calls in during the week, we don't get to call the weekend staff to help us out!"

"Exactly," I said, feeling marginally better already, and settled in to talk all the way to my next patient's home.

By the time I headed to the last patient on my list, darkness had begun to fall. The days were getting longer, but not fast enough to help me out at the moment. I was now in south Dallas, trying to take comfort in the number of police cruisers I was passing. Two of the cruisers in different locations had their blue lights flashing, with a customer or two handcuffed and pushed up against the side of the squad car. I tried to focus on the fact that, thanks to Dallas' finest, some bad guys were off the street and headed to the nearby Lew Sterrett Justice Center, known more for its sturdy bars at the windows and mandatory orange jumpsuits than for its home cooking.

CHAPTER 28

With the VW finally on the highway and the lights of downtown growing smaller in the rearview mirror, belly dancing music began playing its familiar notes from my cup holder.

"Hello?" I said, not taking my eyes from the road to check caller ID.

"Linda, are you okay? Have you left your last house yet?"

"Laura?" I asked, startled by the female voice on the end of the line. I had expected Kevin checking on me rather than the office. Madam Surly's shift must have ended, unlike mine. Laura who was working now still had to assign calls to the nurses, but managed to remember we were all human beings rather than robots. She was concerned for us. "Yes, I just left our patient in south Dallas. He had an enema. I didn't die in a drive-by shooting, so all is well."

"I don't like it when you girls have to go down there at night. I'm going to say something about it. His nurse, I think you know who she is, should have handled that yesterday."

I smiled to myself. Laura would raise holy hell on my behalf.

"I'm guessing you are on Central Expressway. Have you made it to the LBJ Freeway exit yet?"

"Not quite." I sighed silently. "Where am I headed now?"

"Thank you for going. I really hate to ask you, but we had a death in Mesquite and need someone to pronounce. It should be very quick. Greg is the Continuous Care aide there."

"That's good news under the circumstances."

"Yes, it is. Greg will have the situation under control. I really do hate to ask you to do this. If you will just go to Mesquite for me, I won't let anybody call you the rest of the night."

"Laura, you have a deal," I said, thinking of joining Kevin for a late dinner. "Just put the patient's name and address in my pager. I will leave you a voice mail with the time of death and any other details once I get there."

When I had interviewed for this job, the manager at the time asked if I would mind driving as far as Mesquite. I said that was too far to go and if that is where my patients would be located, I would not accept the job. She had agreed, I believed her, and went to work. The funny thing about conversations is if they are not recorded or written down and signed by both parties, they often didn't happen. Initially, my closest patients were in Mesquite. Most were much farther away. So tonight, while the city of Mesquite had not been relocated closer to McKinney, it had become a familiar drive, making it seem closer than it once had.

My pager had been beeping occasionally next to an empty hand sanitizer bottle for a few minutes when I pulled into the gas station parking lot. Ever efficient Laura had paged me the patient name, address, and a big thank you at the end of the message. She knew I was tired and overworked, because so was she. I didn't want to be in Mesquite. Her acknowledgement of that made it a little better.

When you feel cleaner coming out of a dirty gas station unisex restroom than you did going in, it might be time to question life. Having washed off the rest of the enema visit with pink soap and cold water in a rust-stained sink, I bought a bottle of water, and headed back into the night. The patient's home wasn't far and my familiarity with Mesquite guaranteed that I would find it in the dark, even without a visible house number or working porch light, like the dilapidated cockroach hotel I'd just left to the south.

The houses in much of Mesquite were older, probably new at the same time I was. Streets were named for anything and everything having to do with space exploration, another indication of when this area was developed. As I turned off Jupiter Road into the patient's neighborhood, the mature trees that lined the streets were leafy even on a winter's night. That meant they were live oaks, probably the only tree my non-girl-scout-educated mind can identify, unless Christmas tree is counted as a species. Street signs were well illuminated at every turn, simplifying my journey.

When I turned onto the street that matched the street name Laura had paged to me, one house grabbed my attention. It glowed. Every light inside and outside appeared to be on. Cars were parked in the driveway and on the street to both sides of the property. There was either a party or a death. Not infrequently, those events are combined.

I cruised slowly past the illuminated brick ranch. The house number lit by the porch light verified my guess. Pulling past the car at the farthest end, I parked at the curb. Quickly, I rifled through my paperwork looking for a narcotics form. At a death all remaining controlled substances must be counted and destroyed. With the form for wasting narcotics in hand, I headed toward the party house.

I tapped lightly on the door, which swung open instantly. Greg, our nurse's aide, was on the other side. He was dressed as always in blue scrubs and athletic shoes. He stands over six feet tall, and unlike Marcus who I met earlier today, does not appear to have supersized a meal in his life. His shift would have started at eight o'clock this morning, but he looked crisp and clean, unlike the germ-riddled appearance I felt I now presented.

"Come on in, Linda. Good to see you," he said, holding the glass storm door open for me.

"Hi, Greg," I said, looking around to make sure no family members were within hearing range. "This is my last visit at the end of a very long day. When Laura said you were the nurse's aide on duty, I was relieved. If it's you or Twilla working, I know my part will be a piece of cake."

"Maybe not this time," he said, looking down at his shoes.

In spite of our limited contact with each other, I think Greg and I would agree we know each other very well. We have stood together at the bedside of many patients. We have held the wives, husbands, children, and sometimes parents of the patients while their loved one passed away. We have weathered the storm of grief that some family members have raged at both of us. Our interaction has been almost exclusively on the battlefield, where war is fought against cancer, heart disease, and other terminal illnesses. Such extreme conditions provide some decent clues about co-workers. Greg is smart, compassionate, and capable. He also looked distraught, almost tortured at this moment.

That was not a good sign.

"It looks like the whole family is here," I said. We were still standing in the entryway, but hushed voices floated our way from a nearby room. "Were any of the family members a problem?"

Families present a variety of interesting dynamics at a time like this. The family members who were estranged from the patient or just too busy to ever visit usually cause the most trouble. Under the heading of trouble, I've seen screaming, cussing, all forms of ranting and raving, and once a daughter who reported me to Adult Protective Services for murder, while I was in the middle of pronouncing her mother. Fortunately, APS seems very adept at differentiating wild claims screamed into the telephone from real threats to older adults.

"The family is okay, I guess," Greg said.

Something about the disturbed look on Greg's face had told me this was more than a family issue. Fairly certain of the answer, I asked the question. "Did the patient," opening my pager I paused to double check the name Laura had typed in. "Did Mr. Johnson pass peacefully?"

"No, he didn't. Mrs. Johnson is taking it very hard."

"I'm guessing he wasn't in pain," I said, my stomach turning over, anticipating Greg's answer.

"No, it wasn't pain. I know you've seen it, even though we don't see it very often, hardly ever in fact."

Greg's rambling response confirmed the cold chills I was

suddenly feeling inside a very well-heated house.

"Mr. Johnson is, or rather was, very old, in his late nineties. The past few days I've been here with him, the entire family has told me stories about his failing health. He was expected to die twenty years ago when he was in his seventies. Time after time, the doctors predicted his death. He just kept hanging on."

I looked at Greg and back toward the light-filled rooms of the house. Murmurs and occasional sobs drifted our way, but we were thankfully undisturbed by family. We both had enough disturbing thoughts for now to deal with.

"I know at some point in his life, he did something... something very bad, something evil. They all talk around it, but no one ever says what Mr. Johnson is actually guilty of. Mrs. Johnson mentions it the most. She is almost as old as he was, but she sits at his bedside for hours holding his hand. She says over and over that he is only alive because he is so afraid to die."

"How bad was his actual death?"

"Bad. Probably the worst I've seen, and if I'm lucky, I won't see another like it for a very long time, if ever. You've been a nurse for quite a few years, so I'm guessing you know just what I'm talking about."

Unable to focus on and feel concern for a deceased patient I had never met, I nodded yes, and bit the insides of my cheeks to avoid a smile. "Yes, I think I do."

"I could tell he was close. He had all the usual changes in

breathing and vital signs, so there was no way he could hang on any longer. At the point when he should have had his eyes closed and slipped away peacefully, he just raised up in the bed and started screaming."

"Don't let them get me," I filled in for Greg. Greg was holding his hand over his eyes now, trying to shield himself from the horrific scene. My smile went unnoticed.

"Don't let them get me! He yelled it over and over. His face was gripped with agony. He looked like he was being tortured, although he hasn't needed one drop of morphine the whole time I've been here. Finally, he couldn't fight them anymore, whoever they were, and he dropped back on the bed, dead."

Concentrating on the Johnson family, I looked appropriately sad as I thanked Greg and stepped through the living room and into the dining room where most of the mourners had gathered. "Hello, I'm Linda, the hospice nurse," I announced as I entered the room. "I am very sorry for your loss."

A couple of nods and mumbled "thank yous" were directed my way.

"Greg and I will be back in a moment after I've checked Mr. Johnson."

Led by Greg, I made my way to the master bedroom. The hospital bed was set up in the corner of the room. The full-size bed and dresser were shoved to the side at an awkward angle to make room for the newly added equipment. Greg had a sheet spread over the body. Mr. Johnson was obviously dead but I listened for a heartbeat with my stethoscope and felt for a carotid pulse, my fingers resting on a cold, quiet neck. I may sit on a patient's bed, kiss their cheek, and bring them contraband treats, but when pronouncing I always follow procedure. Glancing at my watch, I left the room.

The family, especially Mrs. Johnson, looked expectantly at me as I reentered the room. "The time of death will be 7:32," I said. "I know you have been waiting for me to arrive, but the official time of death is not the last breath, but when I actually pronounce him. I wanted to tell you that so you wouldn't be confused when you saw the death certificate."

"He's dead?" Mrs. Johnson whispered.

"Yes, ma'am," Greg answered for me, kneeling beside the frail lady's chair. She was a small woman who seemed to shrink even smaller with the news she had just received. Her white hair was neatly pinned back in a bun. She was wearing a peach-colored jogging suit that had certainly never seen a track. Her skin was almost translucent in comparison to the ebony arm Greg had wrapped around her shoulder.

"Ma'am, I told you he was gone. You saw him go," Greg said.

"I know, the screaming he did, I just hoped," she paused as though she was trying to find something, anything to give hope. "I guess since you said she had to pronounce him, I hoped maybe you were wrong, Greg. Maybe she would say he wasn't gone."

"No, ma'am, I'm sorry. Greg has done this job a long time. He knew Mr. Johnson was gone. I just make it official. I need to call the medical examiner now and the funeral home. Can you just tell me which funeral home you are using?"

I looked optimistically at the group seated around the maple oval table. A brass container in the center held a slightly dusty arrangement of mauve and blue plastic flowers. Behind the table, thick curtains in colors that matched the flowers were drawn. A few of the men were standing behind the table, pressed against the closed curtains, either due to a lack of chairs or an inability to sit still. Nervous tension filled the room, fueled by the unspoken fears in each mind.

"What happens now?" asked one of the men standing behind the table.

My mention of calling the medical examiner and funeral home had been in very plain English. Unfortunately, a death, even under the best of circumstances, adversely affects hearing and comprehension. "I will call both the medical examiner and the funeral home," I answered slowly. "Greg and I will dispose of any drugs the patient had. Then, Greg will wait with Mr. Johnson's body until the funeral home comes."

The family remained motionless, paralyzed by the grief and fear I saw in their eyes. "Hospice always waits with the body,"

I explained, adding, "And if you would like, we can send a chaplain."

Mrs. Johnson brightened. "Yes, yes. We want the chaplain."

"What denomination is he?" the spokesman from a moment ago asked.

"He works for us in a non-denominational capacity."

"But you know him and you know which church he attends?"

"Yes, he is Baptist."

"Could we get a priest, also?" one of the women asked. We had not been introduced, but judging by her age and seat next to Mrs. Johnson she was either a daughter or daughter-in-law.

"That's a great idea!" our back of the room spokesman added. "I'll call the after-hours number for Mom and Dad's parish church. They'll send us a priest."

He left the room with purpose-filled long strides, followed by the other gentlemen who had been standing with him.

"You don't want the hospice chaplain now?" I asked, unsure of the current plans. I didn't want to call the office for the chaplain unless I had to. The chaplain on call today had already worked a long week, just like me. With any luck, he was sitting down to dinner or watching television with his family instead of making visits at the moment.

"Can I have both?" Mrs. Johnson asked.

I nodded yes, as she continued. "I would like my husband

to stay here until the priest gives him Last Rites. Your chaplain can come at any time. I would really like to talk with him. Maybe he will also pray with us for Mr. Johnson?"

"It, his death, was really bad," the probable daughter interjected. "I think we all knew how afraid he was to die, but still, it was an awful thing to see."

"And hear," another woman added.

"Our chaplain will certainly pray with you. You may also have bereavement visits from him or other hospice staff members throughout the coming year," I added.

"Thanks, but Mom will probably just talk to our priest after today. This was just such a shock for her."

Greg and I excused ourselves to the other room to dispose of the medications and complete the paperwork. "Do you want me to ask the office if you can leave when the chaplain arrives? He could stay with the body until it's picked up," I said once I was sure we were out of earshot.

"No, that's okay. I'll stay."

"It's getting late. Your shift ended an hour ago, and you know they aren't going to replace you with a night nurse to sit with the body."

"Yeah, but I want to stay for Mrs. Johnson," Greg said, just as I would have predicted.

I picked up Mr. Johnson's home chart to take back to the office and said my good-byes to the Johnson family. The house remained aglow as Greg walked me out the door. All the lights in Mesquite, or even in Texas, could not have kept the darkness away from this house today.

"So you knew what happened, at least as soon as I started describing his death," Greg said as we walked toward my car.

"Yes, I think I almost knew just by looking at your face."

"You can tell where they are going, and it is frightening, even for me. I can't imagine what it's like for the patient, and for the family."

"I think to do our jobs you have to believe in heaven. But if you do it long enough, you also learn there really is a hell."

"When did you have a patient die that way?" Greg asked.

"It wasn't a patient," I said, smiling broadly. "It was my uncle."

CHAPTER 29

August 1977

I tossed the battered sky-blue suitcase on the bed. Aunt Muriel and Uncle Karl were both at the convenience store working tonight, so there was no one to yell at me for breaking the law. Beginning tomorrow all those silly rules, like nothing and no one can be on any bed unless they are sleeping would be left behind. Aunt Muriel and Uncle Karl were getting left behind, too.

With both thumbs I pressed on the locks. The suitcase clicked open. Laying it flat, I looked at the two empty halves of the case. It wasn't much room, but I didn't own much either. Besides, I just needed to pack enough to last for about a week.

Then the small foot locker I had just bought would be delivered. The foot locker would definitely hold the winter clothes I'd need later in the semester. For now I opened a drawer and grabbed a small pile of summer tops to pack.

Glancing at the nightstand, I saw two happy faces smiling back at me. I reached for the brass frame and tucked it safely in the pile of shirts. Kevin and I had had our photo taken at a local studio a few weeks ago. It was the first "family" photo I had since Mama got sick. Kevin and I are going to get married. Everyone says we are too young to know who we want to spend our lives with. I might be only seventeen, but I'm not sure I've ever been young.

Next I headed to the little closet. Bypassing the few hanging clothes, I reached into the back corner of the floor. I pulled out a stack of worn spiral notebooks. Most were yellow, my favorite color, with a couple of green and blue ones thrown in. Since I was already a criminal, at least in this house, I took them to the other twin bed and flopped down.

The first date in the oldest notebook took me back to the summer of 1972. The ink scrawled across the page in childish loops. Hopefully I've matured as much as my penmanship in the past few years. I called my diary "Dear Katrina," although how I chose that name I'll never know. I can't remember ever meeting anyone called Katrina.

The first few entries were about swimming, but Mama's

illness quickly took center stage. By the second notebook, Mama had passed away. I glanced at the following pages, skimming but not really reading them. Some pages had pictures instead of writing. The drawings, like the handwriting, were childish. The subject matter, however, was pornographic.

It happened five years ago. The memories remained just as clear as the bowl of cereal I had for breakfast this morning. I had written about Uncle Karl's visits, describing what happened to the best of my ability. Not infrequently, words failed me. I didn't know what was happening, so I drew pictures. Until this summer, only Dear Katrina knew of my shame and suffering.

Many of the entries were about food instead of the abuse. Although thinking about it now, it was really just abuse in another form. While Mama was sick, Nina had lived with Aunt Muriel and Uncle Karl. After the funeral she was moved back in with me. How I was supposed to take care of my elderly grandmother with ever advancing dementia and myself at age twelve was not really clear. Most of my energy went to food procurement. Since the grocery money my sister gave me never went far enough, this topic appeared frequently in my diary. Perhaps if I'd been a bargain hunting coupon maven I could have done a better job. But I was just a kid, I reminded myself yet again.

I came across the entry I made about Nina's death. There was only one. Glancing at it now, it was easy to remember how

I felt at the time. Maybe that's because the feeling hasn't gone away. I loved her and miss her, with those feelings overshadowed by the guilt I feel. I will always feel responsible for Nina's death.

When I was placed with Karl and Muriel by Child Protective Services, she had come along to their house because she needed care much more than I did. Almost instantly, they decided she needed more help than they could provide, so she was placed in a crumbling dark building that had nursing home as part of its name. The place should have been sued for false advertising because it was readily apparent there would be no nursing and no home inside this prison. A better name would have been The Dark Place of Disgusting Smells.

Her suffering and death were things I had never written down, yet never forgotten. While I could and did tell Dear Katrina about my own misery, I couldn't bear to write about Nina. The few times I saw her in that place she was tied to a chair. She had lost so much weight I almost didn't recognize her. She had bedsores from being constantly restrained in one position. Yet, Karl and Muriel seemed to just accept her condition whenever we visited.

A tear splashed on the notebook, which was still open to the page describing her funeral. The funeral was the only thing I had recorded about her last year. I'm sure it was the best part for her, too. If only I had been able to take better care of us. If only we hadn't been reported to CPS. If only I hadn't been just a kid. Maybe my up-coming medical career will somehow atone for Nina's suffering. It's doubtful, but it's all I have.

Wiping my eyes with my hands, I put the notebook back in the pile. Choosing another spiral, I found an entry pointing to the fact that I was just a child. Swallowing some bile along with my last memories of Nina, I took a closer look. After all, it's better to be the injured party than the guilty party any day of the week.

Dear Katrina,

I'm always walking on eggshells. I try so hard to stay out of the way, but I still can't do anything right. Today was just another example of how crazy it is around here. This time, though, you might be surprised at how it turned out.

"Linda, you should be ashamed of yourself! I'm sure your mother is ashamed of you. She's probably rolling in her grave," Aunt Muriel said to me with a mixture of anger and disgust.

I was cleaning the living room at the time of this announcement, and glanced around to see if I had done anything disgusting in the process. Prior to this, I had scrubbed the bathroom. Next I was supposed to start mowing the yard. I know not to complain about the work, even if I occasionally think about changing my name to Cinderella. Dusting already spotless furniture is one of the many tasks I do without question. Questions are not well received.

I had been kneeling on the orange shag carpet as I dusted the coffee table. Aunt Muriel, although petite, was standing and therefore towering over me at the moment. She looked angry. My best guess was this had more to do with something in her head than my efforts at cleaning and yard work. I had tried to do everything just the way she wanted it done. I hadn't cut any corners, and felt blindsided by this attack.

"Excuse me?" I questioned, looking up at her. When she was in one of these moods, it was usually best to say as little as possible.

"You heard me," she spat back. "It's disgusting and shameful. Plain disgusting."

I thought beyond the housework, racking my brain for anything I might have done wrong this week. Volunteering information at a moment like this was dangerous, bordering on suicidal. If I asked, for example, if she was referring to me staying on the phone for an hour or more the other night, and that wasn't the offense, I would have walked into a trap. The long phone conversation would be added to my other, as yet unknown, disgusting offense.

Unable to think of anything that warranted this attack, I surrendered. "What did I do?" I asked, hoping to at least bring the suspense, if not the anger to a conclusion.

"You never call your aunts and uncles."

"What?" I was still kneeling, and it seemed like it might be a good idea to do some praying at the same time. My prayer would be for understanding, because at the moment nothing was making sense.

"You heard me."

"Yes, but I don't know what I did that has you so upset. What about my other aunts and uncles?"

"Your mother was close to her family. They pitched in when she was sick, and you never call them. You don't even try to stay in touch. Like I said, I'll bet your mother is rolling in her grave watching the selfish way you act!"

Slowly I stood. At five and a half feet, I am at least four inches taller than Muriel. I couldn't remember the last time someone in this house even mentioned any of my other relatives. Looking in her eyes I wondered where this sudden burst of anger had started. I wondered why she was so critical of me. I wondered why I couldn't please her.

Then, Katrina, you won't believe what I did. Still staring right back at her I said, "Aunt Muriel, I am the child in all this. They should have stayed in touch with me. I've been here a couple of years now, and they have this phone number and address. If you want to get mad at someone, yell at them."

I dropped my dust rag, walked to the bedroom and closed the door. She never said another word, and I didn't even finish my chores. This turned out to be one of my best days since moving here.

Closing the notebook, I smiled at the memory of that day. I've been living here four years this summer. Aunt Muriel and I get along better now than we did at the beginning. I'm not sure why. I've always suspected she knew what Uncle Karl had been doing. Now that I'm older I can see in some ways she had treated me like "the other woman."

As absurd as that is, this is Kentucky. We all know at least one girl who was married at age thirteen. The fact that my uncle's incestuous acts were criminal doesn't seem to matter. I never told anyone because I couldn't think of anyone who would believe me. Well, Aunt Muriel probably would have believed and blamed me all at the same time. That wouldn't have been particularly helpful.

Besides my diary, I told no one until this summer. One night after seeing a movie, Kevin and I were sitting in his Mustang just talking. I had scooted close to the stick shift so he could put his arm around me. With my head leaning into his shoulder, it all poured out. Once I started telling him, I couldn't stop. I was a broken faucet, tears and words spilling out until there was nothing left to say and no more tears to cry.

He held me for a long time, and I knew what happened somehow hurt him as much as it had hurt me. I didn't want Kevin to suffer like that, but I had to tell him. When he finally took me home, things had changed between us; Kevin and I were now bonded by my shame and the pain I had suffered. We were partners in a crime neither of us had committed. Still, nothing changed between us and Uncle Karl. The only difference was now both Kevin and I had to pretend the whole thing never happened.

I think Karl stopped abusing me when I moved in with him

because he is a coward. It's not like child predators ever have the courage to pick on someone their own size or someone who can fight back. Once I was under his roof, the chance of getting caught by Muriel or her daughter was not something he could risk.

Now if he tried anything, I'd kill him. Kevin wouldn't even get the opportunity.

I've heard of skeletons in the closet, and that is exactly what my Dear Katrina diaries were, and not just because they had been hidden there. The risks associated with keeping them were too great. Pushing my summer clothes to the side in my college-bound suitcase, I made room for all the spiral notebooks. When I got to my dorm, they were headed down the trash chute. My life was now my own, and it was time to take out the trash.

CHAPTER 30

Getting an on-call day over with for the month is equivalent to getting a colonoscopy out of the way. It is scheduled, you know it has to be done, but it is full of excrement all the same. I did make it to C.J. and Sandy's Saturday night in time for leftovers, a glass of wine, and a nap on their couch until it was time to go home. Sunday was swallowed by church, grocery shopping, and laundry. Monday arrived a day early, due to the absence of a real Saturday. Normally, the week following on-call would have been greeted with some lingering exhaustion, but a sigh of relief.

The problem was my next turn for on-call duty was scheduled for Friday night.

It is rumored that a system exists in our office to fairly

schedule the nurses for on-call duty. None of the field nurses are privy to this system, thus making it difficult to question. When we do complain, or in my case, whine about it, we are just reminded that a fair system does indeed exist, shut up about it already, and keep pagers and cell phones turned on. We normally have one weeknight and one weekday of potential extra work in a month. Since this fair (imaginary?) system counts Friday nights as weekdays, even while the rest of the world considers it a start to the weekend, I was technically not working two weekends in a row.

Those thoughts offered little consolation Monday morning as I loaded the VW with supplies from extras I kept on my garage shelves. Courtesy of my visit to south Dallas, I was down to one enema kit in my car, but if I needed more than that between now and Wednesday when I picked up supplies in the office, I really should reexamine my career choice.

With my plastic bins full again, I closed the hatch and climbed in the front seat with a heavy sigh. Picking up my clipboard, I scanned my list of patients. Bonnie's name popped out at me, as I admitted to myself she was rapidly becoming my sickest patient. That made her a Monday visit. Seeing her today would prevent me from worrying about her, and hopefully give me the opportunity to make a second visit this week if it was warranted. Her vital signs were still good. She was still talking, and eating a little at least. She just didn't look good to me. Now that the relatives were there to help out, she was free to give up the fight. It was all a guess of course, but probably a good one. With those thoughts, or rather concerns, bouncing around in my head, I dialed Bonnie's number.

"Hello?" Jim answered after the first ring.

"Hi, Jim, it's Linda. I'm just planning my day, and thought I would swing by to check on Bonnie, if that's okay?"

"Absolutely. We both wanted to see you today."

"Is something wrong? Is she in pain?" My mind raced ahead, swerving through a myriad of possible scenarios that could occur in the last stages of cancer.

"No, no, nothing like that. She just... well, rather I... oh heck. I would really rather she tell it to you. Just come by whenever you want. We'll both be home all day."

"Good. Unless something comes up, I should be there shortly."

There were several routes I could take from McKinney to Sachse. I opted for the winding two-lane back roads. Too late in the morning for school buses, and hopefully too early for much other traffic, I could zip around the curves and be there in no time. It's that bald head, I told myself again, and her young-looking face. She reminds me so much of Mama. There were probably more differences than similarities. Bonnie lost her hair to chemotherapy rather than having her head shaved for surgery. They didn't have the same cancer. They weren't the same age. There was just something there that reminded me of Mama, therefore making me as protective as a mountain lion watching over my cub.

Maybe if Bonnie's kids were more involved I would relax a little. Her in-laws, however, were even better than I had hoped they would be when we first met. Mary hovered over Bonnie, but managed to do it in a way that didn't smother her. She always let Bonnie do as much as she could for herself, while ready to pitch in at any moment. If Bonnie got tired feeding herself, Mary very casually picked up the spoon or fork, and carried on. Mary hadn't confused the terms invalid and child either, as so many people do. She still asked Bonnie's opinion on everything from meal plans and grocery shopping to politics. Just because Bonnie couldn't dress herself, or always feed herself, didn't mean her brain had reverted to that of a toddler.

Ray was just as devoted to Bonnie as Mary was. He was not hands on in caring for her. He helped Jim just by being there. Ray often looked uncomfortable and was known to dart from the room suddenly. In fairness to him, Bonnie's hospital bed was center stage in the cramped living room, and functioned as her bedroom, bathroom, and dining room. The fact that he respected Bonnie's privacy and could blush the color of his brightest plaid pants was endearing.

Still, I would be happier if the children were more

involved. Often in families with several adult children, only one is actively helping. That would be okay with me. If one of Bonnie's daughters or sons had demanded to be called to discuss her condition each time I visited, I could handle that. If they became cross or even angry with me at times because of worry and misplaced anger, I could deal with that too. It bothered me much more that they all stopped by so rarely and visited so briefly, that she might have been diagnosed with small pox or the black plague instead of cancer. I had only to look at my own family, my sister in particular, to see that not everyone handles illness the same. I just wanted one of her children to handle it, at least on some level.

My traffic predictions had come true and I was out of my car and bounding up the steps in no time. The exterior door was open and I could see through the storm door that Bonnie was sitting propped up in bed. Maybe I was better at predicting traffic than Bonnie's prognosis.

"Come on in, Linda," the General said, holding the door open for me. He was so tall that he held the door by the top of the frame, allowing me to walk in beneath his arm.

"Good morning. Where are the in-laws today?"

"Oh, I thought we told you," Bonnie began, holding her arms wide for a hug. Her color looked rosy today, but it could just be a reflection from the pink print on her gown. "They were gone for the weekend, and won't be back until later today.

They made plans months ago to go to Wichita Falls for the eightieth birthday party of Ray's aunt."

"Bonnie's doing so well right now, we told them it would be foolish to change their plans," Jim added.

"You know, we did talk about it one time. I guess I forgot," I said. My thoughts this weekend had been diverted from my regular patients to those on my on-call list. I hadn't even bothered to plan my week. Having hugged Bonnie hello, I settled in my usual chair. "When do they get back?"

"Sometime this afternoon," Bonnie answered.

"Yeah, we told them to take their time and not rush on our account. Besides, Mary does so much for Bonnie, it's about time I had something useful to do," Jim said as he pulled up a kitchen chair and sat down. He was looking expectantly at Bonnie.

"We were fine on our own this weekend, but Jim and I are really glad you wanted to stop by today."

"He said on the phone something was going on but he wouldn't elaborate."

"I hope he didn't have you worried," Bonnie said with a smile.

"No, not really," I fibbed.

"Last night we watched the ten o'clock news, just like we always do," Bonnie began. She was leaning forward, arms wrapped around her legs, looking frail, but more energetic than she had recently. "Then, Jim took Beau for his last walk before we went to bed."

Beau looked up from under Bonnie's bed expectantly at the mention of his name. His shaggy tail thumped the floor a couple of times. When no treats appeared, he settled back down to his nap.

"When Jim and Beau came back in, I asked if he had seen Donald."

"Donald, your oldest son?" I asked.

"That's right. Donald had to work yesterday. He worked late, and on his way home he dropped in for a minute to see me. I told him his dad was walking the dog and that Donald should look for him on his way back out."

"But that's not what happened…"

"Hush, Jim. You agreed to let me tell this. Besides, that *is* what happened."

"Donald was never here," Jim persisted. "I would have seen his car. Not a single car went past while I walked Beau."

"Bonnie, you say Donald stopped by last night, and Jim you say he didn't," I said, attempting to clarify their argument. Bonnie might be taking morphine, but she seemed to be thinking clearly. Besides, a brief visit on the way home from work was totally in character with what I knew of Donald and the other three children. Their daughter Rachel and her cruise flashed across my mind, but I quickly dispelled the useless image accepting that I couldn't change their children.

"So we fussed back and forth about it and finally agreed to disagree. I just figured it was the morphine that had her a little confused," Jim interjected.

"Right, so we went to bed," Bonnie continued. "Then at a few minutes after six this morning, the phone rang."

"That's too early for a friendly call," Jim said. "Any time the phone rings that early or in the middle of the night, I worry that something happened to one of the kids or grandkids."

"I would think the same thing," I added.

"It was Donald," Bonnie said, her smile widening. "He asked if I had a new nightgown."

I looked at Jim who appeared to be as confused as Bonnie was happy. He was shaking his head in disbelief as she continued.

"I said yes I do, as a matter of fact. Then he asked if my new nightgown was lime green with pink flamingoes all over it."

Jim and I both looked toward Bonnie. She had thrown the white sheet back toward the foot of the bed and was holding both arms up to provide a better view. A sea of pink flamingoes was swimming across the creases and folds of the lime green fabric.

"He said he watched the news last night and then went to bed. Then he told me, 'Mom, I crawled into bed, looked up, and saw you. You were standing at the foot of my bed smiling and you were wearing a lime green nightgown with bright pink flamingoes all over it.'"

My breath caught in my throat as Bonnie finished speaking. She and Jim were both looking at me expectantly and I realized neither understood the importance of Bonnie and Donald's shared experience. Arguments have raged for years about near-death experiences and the hallucinations of the dying brain. Survivalists hold that if the mind and the body are separable, we may indeed survive death. Bonnie and Donald had just proven their theory. After all, Donald's brain was thirty-something years old, and he was in all probability decades away from death. His brain was not dying, and not only had they seen each other, he had described a very unusual gown.

"Bonnie, you know what I always tell you, as the body gets weaker…"

"The spirit gets stronger," she finished for me.

"That's right. Jim, you have to believe they saw each other. Of course there wasn't a car for you and Beau to see."

"I know, I know. I just don't understand," he said.

"Jim, you are retired from the military. You are used to strategy and analysis, but this is something that maybe can't be analyzed. It just is what it is," I said, unable to expound on what I believe, but can't comprehend.

CHAPTER 31

Following my visit with Bonnie and Jim, I devoted some time to pondering her story in spare moments throughout the week. Those moments were rare, as I seemed to get busier by the minute. With so much to do the week zipped by, apart from the usual Wednesday morning crawl to the office.

Halfway to the office, or about an hour into the drive, my pager alarmed in the cup holder. "Call Jim," was the entire message.

I pulled off the parking lot posing as a freeway, ready for a hot cup of coffee, and dialed Jim's number.

"Hi, Jim, is everything all right?" My voice sounded calmer than my heart, which was now beating for an uphill walk instead of a phone conversation.

"Linda? Hi, I just thought I should check in with you."

"How is Bonnie?"

"Well, I think she's just fine. Actually, I'm sure of it. She ate an early dinner last night, but hasn't been awake since. Her face looks relaxed, no grimacing. I'm watching for it like I'm supposed to, and so is Mary. Both her forehead and that little space above her nose are smooth as silk. Not a twinge of wincing in sight. Oh, and I'm giving her morphine pills rectally, since she can't swallow, just like you told me to do."

He was repeating the instructions I had doled out little by little in anticipation of this eventual final decline. His voice was steady, and I thought how lucky young soldiers had been to be led by his unwavering strength.

"Jim, it sounds like you're doing just what you need to do. Do you need me to visit, maybe start the around-the-clock care we've talked about?"

"No, I just wanted to check in with you. Misty came by this morning to give her a bath. She pulled the oxygen concentrator out of the closet, and showed Mary and I both how to start the oxygen if we need it. She said her breathing was fine now. We're watching for any changes."

"Wow, it sounds like you really do have it all under control," I said.

"I think so. I'm not going to want the extra care. This little trailer is just too small to have another person in it. Misty gives her a bed bath, and Mary and I can manage the rest."

"I'm going to trust you to call me when you need a visit or more help. Do just what you did today. Call the office, and they will either page me or send a night nurse, depending on the time. And if you ever call, and don't hear back from someone in thirty minutes, call back again."

"Thirty minutes," he repeated.

"Yeah, we don't have lights and sirens, and we aren't even a thirty minute pizza delivery service, but there is absolutely no reason, day or night, someone can't call you back in that amount of time."

"I've got it," he said before we hung up, and I trusted that he did.

Arriving in the frozen tundra, also known as the office conference room, Misty rushed toward me. With my stop for coffee, a restroom, and a call to Jim, the whole team except Dr. Kazi had beaten me there today.

"Linda, Linda! You know about Bonnie? She don't look good. She ain't waking up," Misty said in a single breath.

Misty had me trapped against the wall of windows looking out over Interstate 35. I was gazing longingly at the conference room table, as a place to drop my armload of paperwork, purse, lunch, and other miscellaneous items currently causing cramps in both of my arms. She, however, was worried about Bonnie at the moment, so nothing else mattered.

"I talked to Jim this morning. Let me put this stuff down," I said, attempting to edge toward the table.

"Let's get this party started!" Carol proclaimed, bouncing into the room. "Dr. Kazi just pulled into the parking lot, so we can get going. Who has incident reports to turn in? Misty, go sit down."

"I gave her a bath, but she's not waking up," Misty continued, still standing between me and the table.

The quickest way for Carol and I to obtain our goals was to reassure Misty. "Jim said she had her bath and that you reviewed with him and Mary how and when to use the oxygen. He appreciates your help and so do I. He actually doesn't want Continuous Care because the trailer is too small to hold another person. Besides, he likes having you take care of Bonnie."

Carol and the other team members were watching our little drama unfold. We were rather hard to ignore. Both of us are five and a half feet tall so we were standing nose to nose while everyone else was seated for the show. Misty's voice can usually be heard in the next room, making it impossible to ignore her at this range. Older patients who are hard of hearing find it just about the right decibel level although even a few of those have complained that she routinely shouts.

"Misty, sit down now," Carol repeated.

"Alright," she agreed. "But call me if anything happens to her, and I'll call you to let you know how she's doing when I'm over there."

Reluctantly, Misty stepped aside, taking her seat at the far end of the table with the other aides. As she walked away her dark eyes looked overly bright. She was holding back tears, trying not to cry over Bonnie. We both knew she would sooner or later. They had become close, something I could understand completely.

"Before Dr. Kazi gets here I wanted to say thank you. You all have too many patients right now and they are spread out much farther than they should be. I'm working on it, but there's just no help. I'm trying to get a nurse, maybe an LVN to do some visits, but so far we're on our own. If you get in a real bind, let me know, and I'll try to do some visits on my way home," Carol said.

Carol worked ten to twelve hours in the office every day. Those hours were divided between mind-numbing meetings and being yelled at on the phone by various disgruntled family members. The last thing she needed to do was make visits for us. I'd have to remember to complain less and help more for a while.

That opportunity to help arrived Friday morning with an early call. "Linda, Rhonda has to go see Mrs. Perkins north of McKinney today. If you can do the visit for her, it will save her an hour of travel in each direction."

"Sure, Carol. I like Mrs. Perkins. Besides, I'm on call

tonight, and after last weekend I'm expecting to get called out. I would love to be home before midnight, but I've prepared myself for the worst."

"Good, because I can tell you now, they are still shorthanded. One evening nurse is on vacation and another has called in sick again. Oh, and I was going to page you. Jim, Bonnie's husband, called this morning. He wants to know if you can come by today. I talked to him for quite a while. It sounds like he and the sister-in-law have it under control, but he still wants to see you."

"No problem. She was on my list," I said as I headed my car north to see Mrs. Perkins.

By four o'clock, the office was calling to give me my evening schedule. My favorite weekend administrator was back in the saddle, undisguised glee still in her voice.

"Let's see, there are two patients for you to see at the Plano Medical Center, then after that…"

"I'm still doing my day job, thank you very much."

"I don't know what you think you have left to do. You're mine now. I have visits and you have to make them."

Good. Let's just wage war instead of sniping back and forth I thought, but said, "Right now I'm waiting for a doctor to call me back. I'm in Sachse outside the door of one of Marilyn's patients, because she called in sick."

She probably had a paper cut, or a recurrence of her

allergy to Fridays. Marilyn had a similar allergy to Mondays, but I wasn't going to mention any of this right now to Captain Snippy.

"You need to head over to Plano," she said, both speaking to me and ignoring me simultaneously.

"Look, if I did drive to Plano right now, the first call you would get would be from the patient I'm with now. She is having problems with her heart, and I am not leaving until a doctor calls me back. Then, I have to get her new medication called into the pharmacy."

"I'm telling you…"

Utilizing her technique of ignoring the only other person in the conversation, I continued. "While I am here in Sachse, I'm then going to see my patient Bonnie, who I believe might be actively dying. You don't know about that call either, but trust me, if I don't go there next you will have a General breathing down your neck. When, or if, I get any of this done, I will go to Plano."

Hanging up the phone, my hand was shaking.

After finishing with this patient, I had in all likelihood a dying Bonnie to visit. Hospital patients who had a staff around them to help just didn't seem important at the moment, no matter what the Terminator thought. There was only one possible way to get all this done and I hated to do it.

I called Angela.

"Hey there. Are they working you to death?" she asked, effectively reading my mind.

I gave her a rapid-fire synopsis of the conversation that had just taken place. My words tumbled out, as hurried and jumbled as my thoughts at the moment.

"Let me call you back," she said as the phone went dead.

Staring at the quiet piece of plastic in my hand, I dialed Jim's number. "How is she?" I asked, leaving the hellos and other pleasantries aside.

"Not good, not good at all," was his somber reply.

"I'm with a patient, but I'm only a couple of miles away, Jim. I'll be there as soon as I can."

"I know you will."

If I had been in his shoes, screaming into the phone would have seemed like a good option. His tranquil resolve made me more determined to get there quickly, and stay as long as I was needed. The details of how to accomplish that just escaped me at the moment.

In answer to my unasked prayer, the phone rang. Our medical director was calling me back. "Hi Linda, sorry about the wait. I know I'm covering for Dr. Kazi today, but I'm also attending a conference, so you'll have to make it quick."

What a special day. Not enough nurses *or* doctors to go around. "Dr. Harris, I'm with an elderly patient who takes sublingual nitroglycerin for chest pain. I need to get her started on Nitro-Bid to avoid some of this chest pain in the first place."

"Yes, you do. Twice daily. Call it in."

In record-breaking time, I did just that. I called the hospice pharmacy in Tennessee to ship the drug next week, a local pharmacy to get enough medication for the weekend, explained it all to the family and patient, then wrote the directions down, and ran out the door. If I'd had time to pray, the prayer would have been answered at that moment. My phone rang again, with Angela's name and number displayed on caller ID.

"It all worked out. I called Carol and told her to be prepared for an earful from, what did you call her, the Weekend Terminator? I also told her I would do your on-call visits so you could go stay with Bonnie."

"What? You'd do that for me?"

"Just let me know how Bonnie is."

"I don't know what to say, Angela."

"You're welcome, but instead of chatting, we better get to work," she responded, hanging up before I could blubber my thanks.

Entering the mobile home park, I thought sadly that the trees had not leafed out yet, and that if my suspicions were right they would not turn green again in Bonnie's lifetime. Ray was standing on the porch facing in my direction as I rounded the last bend, one hand shielding his eyes from the evening sun. I had no doubt he was on patrol, scouting for yellow

Volkswagens.

"Glad you're here," he said, opening the car door for me.

The worry on his face and the fact he had met me at the car answered my question. I asked it anyway. "How is she?"

"This is it," he said. "I mean, I don't know much about these things, but you'll see."

I agreed with Ray's assessment of the situation as I stepped across the threshold. "I'm so sorry you had to wait for me. I got here as soon as I could," I apologized to Jim, Ray, and Mary, with eyes only for Bonnie. "I'm going to grab the comfort pack out of the fridge."

Going straight to the kitchen area, I dumped my belongings on the kitchen table and grabbed the box of emergency medications. Opening the box, I found the red-capped bottle I needed, then went to Bonnie's bedside.

"I'm going to give her some Atropine. That should make her breathing quieter. Bonnie, I'm just going to put this in your mouth. It's only a couple of drops that will absorb, nothing you have to swallow," I explained, unscrewing the cap and squeezing two drops in her mouth.

"That's the death rattle," Mary said, her brow furrowed with the pain of watching Bonnie.

"Yes, it is. The good news is she isn't feeling it. I gave her the medicine mostly so you all wouldn't have to listen to it."

Jim was quiet, his eyes also on Bonnie, taking each breath

with her. He was committing every bit of her to his memory. His gaze wandered from her closed eyes, to her lips, and then to her hands as he picked up her small left hand in his. Gently, he rubbed her ring finger and wedding ring as he held her hand. "Is she in any pain?"

"No, she looks comfortable. You've done a good job," I said, resting my hand on his shoulder. "The only thing I think she might like is to have her face washed and put on a clean gown."

"You can do that?" Mary asked. "We told Misty not to come today, because Bonnie obviously wasn't up for a bath. I would have changed her gown. I just couldn't figure out how to do it."

"That's fine. It will just take me a minute. I'll need a washcloth, a gown, and a pair of scissors."

"Oh, that makes sense," Mary said, springing into action.

Lifting the sheet back, I saw Bonnie was wearing a simple white smocked gown at the moment. I smiled knowing I wasn't about to cut the lime green gown with pink flamingoes, and went to work.

The sun set with the four of us sitting around Bonnie's bed. We talked of her life and wondered at the journey she was making now. Whenever I was standing over her to reposition a pillow or wipe her face, I whispered, "Don't forget to say hello to Mama and Daddy for me."

Later that night, with Jim, Mary, Ray, and me praying at her bedside, Bonnie had the opportunity to deliver my message.

CHAPTER 32

Beneath his thick, dark hair were eyes that sparkled, hinting at a secret that was just too good to be shared. His face had always been expressive. I'd seen him nearly freeze the air with a single icy glare. Now, all his energy and emotion radiated warmth. It was impossible to look into his eyes and not smile back. His own smile was constant, unwavering, like the physical outlet for a deep joy welling up inside him. That smile had probably won more than a few hearts, and helped some business deals along as well. He looked now just as I had known him, on his best days, the days he wasn't suffering through his disease.

"Hi, Jack," I said, smiling back.

"Hello," he answered.

"This is real, isn't it?"

"Yeah, it is."

"I mean, I know I was asleep and dreaming. Now that's changed. You're real." Somehow, asking for validation more than once seemed appropriate. This wasn't like hearing Opal's voice or smelling perfume. This was much more. I didn't want to leave any room for doubt when the sobering light of morning broke. Yet, before asking the question, I knew the answer. Dreams can seem real sometimes. This wasn't like that. There is never a moment in the middle of the day when I am talking with someone that I pause to ask, "Is this a dream?"

There was no need to ask now either, except that it was the middle of the night and prior to this encounter I had been sleeping, and Jack was actually dead. Those facts aside, it felt no different than talking to Kevin over a cup of coffee or visiting with Camellia discussing football. I may dream about Kevin or Camellia, but when I'm awake and actually with them, I know it. I don't think I've ever bothered to verify I wasn't dreaming.

"You're not dreaming now. I am here."

In spite of the peace and joy I felt in his presence, my mind raced. This was a miraculous opportunity. I searched for a way to further validate what was happening, to extend our contact, yet somehow knowing there were very distinct limits to what I was going to learn from this encounter.

"If you're real and this is happening, give me a hug."

Being a hospice nurse isn't like other jobs. Hugging patients and their families, or in the case of my older ladies at the Ranch, a hello and good-bye kiss, goes with the job. I was seeing him and hearing him. Touching would add another layer to the experience. Besides, there was a part of me that was curious about the possibility of touching someone who had gone. He looked alive, only better, more vibrant. But was he real enough to touch?

"Sure," he replied, and before I knew it, his arms had me wrapped in a brotherly bear hug. I hugged Jack, not just air, but him. I had half, or more than half, expected him to blow away. I thought my arms would wrap around nothing except my own shoulders.

He looked alive, sounded alive, and now he felt alive. I tried to reconcile what was happening with what I knew to be possible, or thought I knew. I had seen my mother four years after her death, but I had never before seen a patient who had died. Yet, I knew I had seen my mother, just as I knew Jack was with me now.

Stepping back, he said, "I need you to do something for me."

"What is it?" A million other questions should have popped into my head. What is heaven like? Is there a God? What is it like to die? At the moment, however, my only focus was Jack. Any curiosity I had was focused on him and the reason for this visit. It was just as well I didn't pose any of those other questions. They weren't the reason for his visit, and weren't likely to be answered.

"I need you to tell my mom that I'm in heaven," he said, looking me directly in the eyes.

"Of course you're in heaven." That made absolutely no sense, and certainly did not justify his visit. This was a heck of an effort to make to state the obvious. He might as well have told me to visit Betty and inform her that the grass was green and the sky was blue with occasional white puffy clouds.

"I know, but I need you to do this. Just tell her I'm in heaven."

"This doesn't make any sense. You died, Jack. You're in heaven. Everybody knows that."

"So you'll tell her for me?"

"I'll tell her."

"Oh, and one more thing. Tell her heaven isn't somewhere else. It's right here. It wouldn't be heaven if we had to leave the people we love."

When I opened my eyes the next morning, the memory of Jack's visit came rushing back. I looked at the ceiling and remembered our conversation. Seeing Jack had been peaceful. Although it had not disturbed my night, it was wreaking havoc with my morning. How on earth was I going to tell Betty that her dead son stopped by to tell me he was in heaven?

More importantly, why on earth would I do that?

Being a nurse requires a certain amount of sanity. Speaking of Jack's visit seriously jeopardized my claim to any thread of sanity at all. I mean, what's the opening line here? "Hi Betty, just wanted to call and tell you Jack said hello from heaven."

While I had promised Jack that I would do his bidding, I valiantly tried to talk myself out of it. My most compelling argument centered on my role as messenger. Man dies. Man goes to heaven, or the after-life, or whatever you want to call it, and has a message for someone he left behind. If he has the ability to tell me, why did he not go to Betty directly? It seems that eliminating the middleman is the surefire way to get the message delivered.

The answer was obvious, even if I didn't like it. Betty trusted me, probably more than she trusted anyone else, including herself. If Jack visited her, she would dismiss it as a dream, or wishful thinking. If I visited her and delivered his message, it would be much harder to ignore. There's a possibility as well, that some people are more receptive to such communications. From smelling perfume to seeing my mother, I have had more than my share of otherworldly experiences. Children, like Manuel's and Mike's grandchildren, seem the most open to these things. My theory has always been that losing my parents as a child enhanced this gift in some way.

When I tell patients and families about one of these strange experiences, they sometimes have a story to share in return. They have seen a person who has died, or talked to them, or maybe just had a sign. These experiences are labeled as dreams, even if they happen in the full light of day. Communicating with a person who is dying or has died is just too insane to talk about in any context other than a dream. Jack wasn't willing to risk that with Betty. Yet for some unknown reason, he felt compelled to tell her he was in heaven.

Looking over at Kevin sleeping soundly, I wanted nothing more than to pull the quilt up and snuggle safely next to him. Reluctantly I sat up instead. There was something profoundly peaceful in Jack's visit, and putting my bare feet down on the cold wood floors seemed like a harsh return to earth. I plodded down the hall to the kitchen and made coffee. The smell of vanilla bean coffee floated in the air, real, but no more so than Jack had been a few hours earlier.

Showered and wrapped like a mummy, my hair in a thick white towel, ankle-length white robe tied tight at my waist, I returned to the kitchen. Kevin was up now, sitting at the table, reading his e-mail. Pouring a cup of coffee, I perched in the chair next to him.

"Good morning."

"Good morning, Sweets. How did you sleep?"

"Jack was here."

He looked up from his laptop, and met my gaze. There was

no trace of doubt in his eyes, nor did I expect to see any. "Jack, your patient? The one who died? Betty's son?"

"Yep, that would be the one," I said, taking a fortifying sip of coffee. I needed a good jolt of caffeine.

"He touched you on your shoulder the other time," Kevin continued in an apparent attempt to wrap his mind around Jack's latest visit to our bedroom.

"Yes, that was the day he died."

"I remember. Did he do that again?"

"No," I said, suddenly fascinated by the contents of the mug in my hands. I stared into the coffee, wishing for something sane to say. "He talked to me this time. I also asked him to hug me, so I would know it wasn't a dream."

"Did he? Did he hug you?"

"Yeah, he did. It was just as real as hugging you. Now I wish I had thought to have Mama hug me when I saw her."

Kevin was looking at me thoughtfully. He was giving me his undivided attention, but more importantly, his trust. "What did he want?"

"That's the problem," I said with an audible sigh. "He wants me to go see Betty. I'm supposed to tell her he's in heaven."

"Of course he's in heaven."

"I know, I know. My task is to be the messenger of the obvious. The only other thing I'm supposed to tell her is, 'Heaven isn't somewhere else. It wouldn't be heaven if we had to leave the people we love.'"

"Well, that should be comforting to her, at least. How do you think she'll take it?"

"I really don't know. It was wonderful to see him, so peaceful, just like seeing Mama. You always believe me when strange things happen, but what if Betty thinks I'm a lunatic? Besides, it just doesn't make any sense. Jack is in heaven. Where else would he be?"

"I don't know, Sweets."

"I do believe in hell. I'm convinced of its existence, and also of its rarity. Betty couldn't think someone like Jack would go there," I said, thinking out loud.

"You have to go see her and give her Jack's message, even if it doesn't make sense to you."

"What if she thinks I'm crazy?"

"She won't," Kevin said, reaching across the table to squeeze my hand.

"I don't know. I guess I do have to go, but it can't be today. I just can't manage another visit."

My one-day reprieve from delivering Jack's message soon turned into a week. There were the normal delays: sick patients, admissions, team meeting, weekend time off, grocery shopping, housework, car washing, paperwork, organizing my spice rack, getting my haircut, and so on. At the point I was ready to pull all of my supplies out of the car to reorganize them and make second visits to patients whether they needed them or not, I realized I had to go see Betty. My hope had been that by delaying the visit, something would change. Ideally, I would have convinced myself it was all a dream. Sanity would return. The world would be as it should. Dead people would stay dead. I would be employed as a nurse, not a messenger.

No chance.

If I hadn't asked Jack to hug me it might have felt less real. I doubted it. I was left with memories of a conversation, not of a dream. Dreams have a transparency, a filmy feel. Daylight comes and the haze of remembered dreams burns off like morning clouds. Dreams lack substance, making it difficult to remember something that didn't happen in the first place. My talk with Jack wasn't like that. It was more like a conversation with Kevin, or with anyone else still breathing for that matter. I could remember the words we spoke, the inflection in our voices.

Sitting at the kitchen table one evening, twirling spaghetti instead of eating it, I finally said, "I have to go see Betty."

Kevin was watching me play with my dinner, not my usual response to food. He hadn't questioned my lame excuse for not going to church on Sunday. He knew as well as I did I was terrified of confronting Betty. He smiled at me, hopefully proud that I had relocated my backbone, and said, "Yeah, you do."

"She's going to think I'm psychotic."

"Probably not. She likes you, and you took good care of her son."

"I hope you're right," I said and finally took a bite.

Kevin's lack of concern over my plight strengthened my resolve. If there were cause for alarm, he would be the one breaking the glass and pulling the red lever. First thing the next morning, I called Betty. Now that I had decided to see her and deliver Jack's obvious statement, I wanted nothing more than to get it over with.

"Betty, hi, it's Linda."

"Linda, I missed you and Kevin at church Sunday. I was really hoping you would be there."

"Yeah, I'm sorry we missed you. Something came up," I said, not adding that the something was merely my cowardice. "Listen, I'm sure I mentioned that part of hospice is bereavement services."

"Yes, and your chaplain called. Tom was his name. He's a very sweet man. He talked about Jack, or rather, let me rattle on about Jack. I told Tom that I didn't need him to visit. I may talk to the priest at St. Jude. I'm not sure."

"Actually Betty, I was hoping I could make a bereavement visit to you today."

"That would be lovely. I miss having you stop by the house. Will you come in the afternoon like you always did?"

"Sure, I'll see you this afternoon. Bye," I said.

For now, I would just put on extra deodorant in anticipation of a morning of waiting, filled with heavy sweating. My stomach wasn't feeling so hot either, and it had nothing to do with the gallon of coffee sloshing around in it.

Pulling into Betty's neighborhood that afternoon, my stomach was making more noise than my car. Sitting between the stone pillars, I shifted into first gear as I waited for the gate to swing open. My friendly guard was at the helm and walked over to the car.

"Haven't seen you lately," he said, leaning in the window.

Today? Today? Really? Today you want to settle in for a nice chat? Can't someone be calling you on your cell phone to distract you?

In answer to my aggravated wishes, his phone rang and he stepped back from the car holding the phone in the air. "I need to take this," he whispered in unnecessary apology.

The gate was now three quarters open, so I rolled in its direction before either my common sense or yellow belly instincts could intervene. The neighborhood speed limit is only twenty miles an hour, I noticed for the first time as I eased through the gate. No time like the present to obey the law. Slowly, like a new driver behind the wheel for my maiden voyage, I took the right turn toward Betty's house. The houses in the development are all stamped from similar, yet very picturesque, cookie cutters. The stone and gabled facades would be considered quaint if they were smaller and not surrounded by lush fairways.

When I finally arrived at Betty's house, having shifted no higher than second gear, I drove up the driveway just as I had many times before and pulled on the emergency brake. Gathering my courage, I decided I had no choice but to commit professional suicide. I could hear Betty's call to the Texas Board of Nurse Examiners now. In between sobs she would say, "This lunatic, a registered nurse who cared for my dying son, claims to have seen him since he died."

Actually, I couldn't really imagine Betty doing such a thing. She was much too kind and too spiritual for that. Probably. That was just the response ninety-nine percent or slightly more of all people would have if they received a visit of this nature. Sometimes, though, stupid and inevitable are kindred spirits. I was going to do this. I promised Jack. My only hope was that it would, by some wonder, transform from a stupid to a rational act. The possibility, however, seemed remarkably remote.

I pushed the doorbell, miraculously causing the door to swing open. Betty had, of course, been watching for me from the window as she often did when I was coming to visit Jack. As quickly as the heavy wooden door could swing open, I was enveloped in her arms.

"I missed you," she gushed as she held me tight. "Today was

the perfect day for you to visit. I've been blubbering around like an old fool, missing Jack, missing my other son Andrew. Just feeling sorry for myself."

"I missed you too, Betty," I said softly. It bothered me more than a little that her son who had died as a child shared the same name as my own son.

"Come on in," she said, releasing her hold on me. "I put the kettle on to make us some tea. Remember when that Chinese doctor was riding with you? We had a lovely time over a cup of tea."

"Yes, I remember her. I was supposed to be teaching her hospice so she could implement it in China, but all she wanted to talk about was my daughter, Nicole."

"That's right," she said with a small laugh. "Still, I was very impressed that Jack's hospice nurse was training her."

"Then you're easily impressed, Betty," I said with a smile. It was good to see her again, in spite of my fears.

"Come on, I hear the kettle whistling for us."

I followed her down the hallway to the kitchen and family room area. Betty was wearing a lavender pantsuit today with a white blouse, and of course, a jaunty scarf in Monet hues tied neatly at her throat. A slim bow of darker purple restrained her hair. I gave a sideways glance at the adjoining spaces as I followed her back the well-known path. There had to be a matching purse lurking somewhere on a chair. She had lost another son but sorrow had not emerged as the victor. Betty was a survivor, and a well-coiffed one at that.

"Sit down over there and I'll just get our tea," she said, indicating the empty sofa. The entire room, although still filled with glossy cherry tables and upholstered furniture, felt empty without Jack. I took my seat where Jack should have been propping his swollen feet on the ottoman. The only new accessory in the room was a cardboard box of tissues, half-empty, on the coffee table.

My mouth suddenly felt parched in spite of the fact I had been sipping water all the way here. I tried to swallow, the meager saliva catching halfway down my throat. "Betty," I stammered, my voice cracking with the desert dryness.

"Yes? Here is your tea. I made Earl Grey. I hope that's alright?" she replied, settling herself in the chair across from me.

I gulped the scalding liquid in an attempt to lubricate my faltering voice. Instead I scorched my tongue, rendering me unable to taste jalapeños on a pizza for at least a week. "Betty, I have to tell you something."

She looked startled by my bluntness and probably knew me well enough to see my nervousness. To her credit, she only said, "What?"

"Jack came to see me," I rushed on before my nerve ran out the door ahead of me. "He came to see me about a week ago."

Betty was a smart woman. It wouldn't in fact take brilliance to do the math. Jack had been very dead a week ago. He had been just as dead two weeks ago. Now at least, I had the insane part out there. I looked into her eyes, which were already welling with tears.

"You saw Jack?"

That was good. She had that part.

"Yes, I saw Jack."

"He was dead a week ago."

"Yes, Betty. I know it's hard for you to believe. It's just as hard for me to accept. Anyway," I said in one breath. I had to get this out. "He wanted me to come see you. In fact, he gave me a message to deliver to you."

"Jack," she whimpered, as I reached into the box of tissues and handed her one. The tears had already begun a free fall down her cheeks.

"He's in heaven, Betty. That's what I'm supposed to tell you. I know it doesn't make any sense, and I'm so sorry to cause you more pain."

Her silent tears grew, morphing into sobs of anguish as I finished that last sentence.

"Betty, I am sorry," I said, trying to imagine a time in my life, past or future, when I could possibly be more sorry than I was at the moment.

Clutching the disintegrating tissue to her face with one

hand, she held up the other hand, gesturing for me to stop. I clamped my mouth shut before I could repeat again just how sorry I was to inflict further pain on her. I wanted to step around the coffee table and wrap her in my arms, but for the moment I was paralyzed. The agony of what I had done to this innocent mother had rendered me unable to move. Her outstretched hand prevented me from speaking, although words did not exist that would erase the heartache I had caused.

With no other option available, I sat quietly on her couch, gazing at the tops of my scuffed black leather shoes. Watching her tears was more than I could bear. Finally, after an extensive study of my plain shoe tops, I heard what I thought was a crack of her voice. I met her gaze sheepishly and saw her strength returning. She stiffened her spine, held her head up, and looked directly at me. Betty, the Survivor, was back. The remaining tears were thrust away as she once again took charge over sorrow.

"Jack wanted you to tell me he is in heaven?" she asked quietly, but without hesitation.

"Yes, that's what he said. I know it doesn't make any sense."

"Actually, it makes perfect sense," she interrupted. "I'm sorry I fell apart. I think you will understand once I explain."

Perfect sense she said. There was nothing either perfect or sensible about the message I had received and delivered. I leaned forward on the couch now, closer to Betty, hanging on her every word. I was waiting for something, an explanation, understanding, maybe even a dose of reality. Her composure had returned, and I wanted desperately to feel as peaceful as she now looked.

"You know I am Catholic. Jack would have said I went a little overboard on catechism and doctrine."

I smiled to myself, remembering sitting outside with Jack joking about Betty being more Catholic than the pope.

"So as a Catholic," Betty continued, "I should have been praying for the repose of his soul. I should have had Masses said for him at church. I should have done those things, but I didn't."

I looked up at Betty, not sure of what I would see. She embodied grace under fire. She, who had suffered the unimaginable sorrow of losing two sons, knew how to hold her head up and maintain her dignity and beliefs. A major part of that was her faith, which while it might seem ritualistic, was true and unwavering. A Betty who didn't follow the expected norm was someone I had not yet met.

"I wanted to pray for his soul, I really did. I thought about it time and time again. I just couldn't do it," she confessed, hands folded now in her lap, her eyes cast downward.

I caught my breath and watched her. If there were words that would offer her consolation, they weren't popping into my blank mind.

"So instead of praying for Jack, I just sat here, and over and over asked for a sign. Just let me know if he is in heaven, I kept asking. I don't even know if I was talking to God or Jack or the walls. I just couldn't stop asking, pleading. That's not even the first box of tissues I went through. Is he in heaven? I couldn't think of anything else. It was a broken record, playing non-stop in my mind."

Feeling had returned to my limbs as she spoke. I hoisted myself from the couch cushion and knelt beside her. Holding her hand in mine, I said, "I'm really sorry I didn't come to tell you sooner. I was afraid."

"Oh, don't be sorry. Thank you! Thank you for telling me," she said, pulling her hand from mine and wrapping both arms around me.

"Betty," I said, pulling back so I could again see her eyes. "I'm supposed to tell you one more thing. Jack said, 'Heaven isn't somewhere else. It wouldn't be heaven if we had to leave the people we love.'"

She reached around me and pulled another tissue from the box. She dabbed at her eyes, the stream of tears reduced to a few random drops of moisture. She sniffled slightly and said, "So that means he is with me now."

"That is what he said, and since I saw him, he must be here."

"That means my son Andrew... he is also with me," she

added, verbally connecting the dots of Jack's message.

Sitting back on the couch, I picked my teacup back up. Sipping from the delicate china, we sat in companionable silence for a moment. I knew as Betty glanced around the room, her thoughts were on both of her sons. They were with us, and so were Mama and Daddy.

Betty smiled as she placed her cup and saucer on the table. Her tears were gone and I had a hunch they weren't going to make a return. The box of tissues was no longer needed. "Jack is in heaven, but because he loves me, that's right here."

"That's right," I said. "Life after death seems simple, even obvious now, and so much better than the pictures we've tried to paint of it. Heaven is here, and it is love."

EPILOGUE

Summer was not only hot, it was determined. The calendar stated plainly that fall had arrived, but the thermometer in my car said the temperature was just shy of one hundred degrees. I was headed to the Ranch, which might or might not provide relief from the heat. My newest patient, Dorothy, was in her upper nineties and seemed to prefer her room temperature the same number as her age. This summer she had even kicked on the gas fireplace in the dining room until the Ranch maintenance men figured out a way to lock the switch.

I was approaching the left hand turn for the Ranch, when I turned right instead. If the driver behind me was irritated by the lack of a turn signal, he didn't honk his displeasure. The sign with the golden arches had locked me in its tractor beam at the last minute with the promise of an ice cold beverage dispensed in a cup the size of a small bucket.

I pulled into one of the angled parking spaces, and rearranged the contents of the passenger seat, hiding anything with personal information on it. I pulled my stethoscope off, tossed it on top of the organized chaos, and climbed from the car.

"Don't worry. She's just like us."

I stopped dead in my tracks. Looking right and left, I saw no one nearby, nor did I expect to see anyone.

I whispered, "What?" but the only response was the rush of highway traffic. Putting my hand on the hatch of the car to steady myself, I continued to look around, thoughts of cold beverages and afternoon patients evaporated by the simple statement.

It was Mama.

I knew her voice as well as I knew my own face in the mirror. I also knew she was referring to my daughter, her granddaughter, Nicole. Blinking in the bright sunlight, I continued to look around the parking lot. I wasn't going to see her this time, and the inflection in her voice told me the message was complete, at least for now.

"Don't worry. She's just like us," I repeated to myself. Well, I wasn't worried about Nicole, at least not before pulling into the parking lot. Now I was beginning to panic. Mama had said she would be there when I needed her. Exactly why did I need her now?

The rest of the message assuaged that worry, at least to a degree. If Nicole was like "us" that meant I was like Mama. I would rather be like Mama than like anyone else on the planet. She was strong, wise and loving. Kevin once said I idolized her because she died before I was a teenager. He said that's when most people first see the flaws in their parents. He was wrong about Mama. If she had not been such an amazing mother, I pointed out, how could I have ever survived the rest of my childhood? The love and strength she gave me had been my life preserver.

Unable to infer anything more from a handful of words, I went inside to order my drink and continue my day. When I finally reached the Ranch, I was grateful it was quiet, since I was somewhere south of preoccupied.

Arriving home that evening, I let Biscuit out and headed to the bedroom to ditch the lab coat and long pants in favor of something cooler. Passing through the kitchen, I heard, "You don't have to be with her all the time now. I wasn't physically present with you, and look at how you turned out."

Thoughts of comfortable clothes forgotten, I settled in a kitchen chair and kicked off my shoes. Mama. It was Mama and yet another comment about Nicole. And me. I was having trouble concentrating on Nicole at the moment. Mama is proud of me.

I circled back to the end of her remark. "Look at how you turned out."

It may seem like a small comment. To me, it was the world. Besides Kevin, not a lot of people have been proud of me. I do realize what I have accomplished, and sometimes think it would be less surprising if I had become a hooker instead of a nurse, based on the abuse I'd endured. According to Aunt Muriel I never did anything right, my sister hasn't spoken to me in decades, and Uncle Karl, well the only thing I can say about him is that he had the good sense to die six weeks after Nicole was born. Her birth was a trigger, one that I was ready to pull. Until then, it never occurred to me he could, and probably had harmed other girls. I was going to take him down, but the devil beat me to him.

When Nicole was only six weeks old, I received a phone call from Kentucky. I knew Karl had been in the hospital, but the news was still unexpected. He had died. He just hadn't slipped away peacefully. Most of the information imparted by my cousin centered on his actual death. He had a cardiac arrest, was resuscitated, and came back screaming, "Don't let them get me!"

They got him.

He arrested again, and could not be resuscitated a second time. Kevin and I, along with two-year-old Andrew and baby

Nicole went across the country to the funeral. We had to make certain for ourselves the bastard was stone-cold dead.

In spite of all those struggles, I had survived. Mama was happy enough with how I had turned out to tell me. So what exactly was going on with Nicole? Of course I'm not with her all the time. She's at college. I don't worry about her at college. Should I?

I thought about my patient Jack. He had said, "Heaven isn't somewhere else. It wouldn't be heaven if we left the people we loved." His mother and I had both been comforted at the time by his statement. Mama's message confirmed what Jack said and proved she loved me, and is still with me. Now if I could only figure out what Nicole has to do with this.

When I checked with Nicole, she told me everything was "fine," the word kids use to technically answer parents' questions without saying anything at all. In hindsight, I suppose she was fine at that moment. Even she didn't know the twists and turns her life was about to take.

At Christmas break, she told us she was breaking up with her boyfriend and changing schools. She stayed home to attend the local community college for a semester. The next semester she transferred out of state. The new boyfriend, actually an old high school crush, was stationed near the new school. Then, when she was twenty and the boyfriend was nineteen, they married.

Panic is a small word for the big fear that swept through me. Through it all, Mama's words played like a broken record in my mind. "Don't worry. She's just like us."

Mama and I both found our true loves as teenagers, but times have changed, haven't they? Mama got married at sixteen to Daddy who was eighteen. I met Kevin when I was sixteen and he was seventeen. Nicole met her husband when they were sixteen and seventeen. Daddy was in the Army Air Corps, while my new teenage son-in-law is in the Air Force. None of this is what I had dreamed for Nicole, and certainly not at her age.

A working knowledge of geometry isn't needed to see the parallel lines in our stories. Yet, I keep hoping the "just like us" part includes more than ages and branches of the military. Being just like Mama goes beyond the statistics. It means loving life and family so much even death is not a barrier.

ACKNOWLEDGEMENTS

My husband Kevin has given his unwavering support to me throughout our life together, but especially through the joyful and sometimes painful process of writing this memoir. He really would be the one to break the glass and pull the red lever if there were cause for alarm!

I'd also like to thank my team of editors. Sallie Randolph provided both legal advice and encouragement. My editor Kathleen Groom skillfully decided what stories to cut, while urging me to add more of my childhood. Her powers of persuasion are impressive.

Rebecca Keeling, Rosemary Kirchner, and Lura Fischer pored over the manuscript word by word. Mia Manns did a brilliant job on the final proofread, finding those last few needles in the haystack.

Finally, I'd like to thank all the patients and families I've worked with during my nursing career. Nursing was my accidental occupation, but you helped make it my vocation.

**Photographs from this memoir are available at
lindakinnamon.com**